Beauty in the $\mathcal{H}eart$

A Study of Godly Beauty for Young Women

Pam Forster

Doorposts

Much of this book was included in *Beauty and the Pig: A Study of Godly Beauty* by Pam Forster, published in 2003. These studies have been completely re-written and re-organized, and notes on using free online study tools have been added.

ISBN 978-1-891206-46-7 (print edition)

ISBN 978-1-891206-47-4 (PDF eBook edition)

Doorposts
5905 SW Lookingglass Dr.
Gaston, OR 97119
www.doorposts.com
888-433-4749

For my granddaughters
Katie, Ruby, Virginia, Victoria, Elanora,
and all the other little princesses-to-come!

In the blink of an eye, you'll all be ready for these studies.
I love you all!

Nana

Thank You

To my family, who graciously lived with me while I worked on this.

To Daniel who didn't just say "we need to finish this,"
but did everything a man could possibly do to help make it happen.

Table of Contents

Introduction

This collection of studies is primarily for women, and especially for girls and young women, (although young men will benefit from its study of the true godly beauty they should seek in a wife).

Most women are interested in being pretty. It doesn't matter what age we are. Almost from the cradle, we enjoy the little things that make us feel beautiful. Tiny hair bows and twirly skirts, sparkly crowns and puffy sleeves gradually give way to finding the perfect hairstyle and fragrance, the most slenderizing dress style, and the most flattering makeup. We all want to do what we can to look our best.

There's nothing wrong with looking our best. God is the one who made beauty. He approves of it! But He's even more interested in what is happening in our hearts.

This collection of studies is about doing all we can to be our best. The truest beauty comes from our hearts. No matter how hard we work to be beautiful on the outside, if our hearts aren't right with God and right with people, we won't really be beautiful. A rebellious, selfish heart usually shows.

The book will help you accomplish two important things:

It will help you grow to understand beauty. God is the giver of beauty, and He wants us to understand what *true* beauty is and where it comes from. These studies will help you learn what *God* says about beauty in the midst of a beauty-obsessed world.

It will help you learn how to study the Bible. This book is designed to give you experience in many different approaches to Bible study. When you have completed the book, you will not only know more about godly beauty. You will also know how to continue studying the Bible on your own. The more you read and study and obey God's Word, the more you will become like Jesus.

***That* will be truly beautiful.**

If you learn to trust like Jesus, humble yourself like Jesus, serve like Jesus, and love like Jesus, it will show on your face. The beauty of a heart that loves Jesus is a beauty that doesn't fade. It only grows more and more beautiful.

As you learn about beauty, you will also learn how to:

- Compare one passage of Scripture with another

- Observe repeated words and themes in a passage

- Outline the content of the passage

- Gather all of Scripture's words about a particular topic

- Study the lives of people in the Bible, noting how their attitudes and actions portray the truths of Scripture

- Study original Hebrew and Greek words and how they are used in other places in Scripture

- Use printed and online study helps in your Bible study

- ...and much more!

How this book works:

This book consists of nine studies, with a short review study at the end. Each study is divided into daily assignments which take from five to twenty minutes each. The book contains 86 days worth of study (about 17 weeks if you do five studies a week). You may complete more than one assignment per day if you want to finish faster. Ideas for additional study are given at the end of each study (a total of 49), giving enough direction for up to a whole year of meaningful Bible study.

Using Computers for Bible study:

Digital Bible study tools are becoming more available and affordable, and if you use the Internet, you can find most of the study tools that you'll need for free. These tools can help you study more thoroughly and efficiently. The studies in this book are based on printed study tools, but each study gives optional instructions for using digital Bible study tools (in the gray boxes in the sidebar).

Recommended materials:

To fully benefit from these studies, you will need *Nave's Topical Bible* and *Strong's Exhaustive Concordance*. Both books are valuable study tools that you will use over and over again, and they are worth the investment. You can find these books online, at most Christian bookstores, or possibly from your church library. We also offer inexpensive hardbound editions at www.doorposts.com.

Several studies require you to mark words or verses in your Bible, so you will need a Bible that you don't mind marking in and some colored pencils or non-bleeding highlighters.

Bible translations:

The studies in this book use primarily the King James translation of the Bible because of the many study tools available for this translation. If you prefer to study in a different translation, search for study tools like a concordance and a topical Bible that are designed for your translation. These are becoming increasingly available.

Recommended age levels:

The studies in this book are designed for ages 10-12 and up. Younger girls may be able to complete the studies with help from a parent, older sibling, or teacher.

For families with boys:

This study is written primarily for young women, but it's also appropriate for young men. Young men can encourage young ladies to grow in true, godly beauty. They also need wisdom to discern between true and false beauty in their relationships and as they consider marriage. In a few places, alternate questions for young men are indicated with "✳". These alternate questions are found in the back of the book.

Study 1

Beauty in Submission

An Inductive Study of 1 Peter 2:11–3:9

"For to this you have been called, because Christ also suffered for you, leaving you an example, so that you might follow in his steps." (1 Peter 2:21, ESV)

The Bible has quite a bit to say about beauty. Our study of godly beauty in this book will center on several specific verses – 1 Peter 3:3-4, 1 Timothy 2:9-10, Proverbs 11:22, and Proverbs 31:30-31.

To start our study of godly beauty, we will be using a simplified version of the inductive study method to study a portion of 1 Peter. This will help us better understand the context of 1 Peter 3:3-4 before we study it in detail in Study 2.

Day 1 - Pray and read

In this first lesson, we are going to read the entire book of 1 Peter to get an overview of its message. This book is a letter. We will understand it better if we learn about its author, its recipients, and its historical background.

A. Read the entire book of 1 Peter.

B. Find answers to these questions in the text:

How does Peter describe himself?

_____

_____

_____

_____

To whom did he write this letter?

_____

_____

Find a Bible map that shows these areas in Asia Minor. What is this area of the world called in our day?

_____

Inductive Bible Study:

1. Read and observe

2. Interpret and organize

3. Apply

What you will need:

• Bible

• Bible atlas or online maps

• Study Bible or Bible commentary

• Colored pencils

• English dictionary

According to chapter 5, why did Peter write this letter?

_____

_____

_____

C. Using a commentary or study Bible, find answers to these questions about the background of 1 Peter.

When did Peter write this letter? _____

Where, most likely, was Peter when he wrote this letter?

_____

Was Peter writing to Jews or Gentiles? _____

Who was emperor of Rome at the time? _____

What was happening in Rome at the time?

_____

_____

_____

_____

Day 2 - Observe

Six questions to ask when reading:

- Who?
- What?
- When?
- Where?
- Why?
- How?

We've read the entire book of 1 Peter and learned a little bit about its background. Now, before we focus specifically on 1 Peter 3:3-4, we are going to spend some time studying the context of those two verses on godly beauty. We are going to read 1 Peter 2:11-3:9 several times, and we are going to **ask questions** of the text in order to understand it better.

Several questions will help us when we approach any passage of Scripture. This list of questions is often used by journalists, researchers, and investigators, and is sometimes referred to as "Five W's and an H". These questions help a person gather objective facts about a situation or subject. None can be answered with a simple "yes" or "no".

When studying a passage of Scripture, we want to look objectively at what is actually there in the text. Depending on the type of passage we are reading, we can look for answers to the following kinds of questions:

- **Who?** Who is in the story? Who is being addressed by the writer? Who is the writer? Who are different specific instructions directed to?

- **What?** What happened? What were the people trying to do in the story? What is the writer's purpose? What is the writer saying to his readers? What is the writer telling his readers to do or not do?

- **When?** When did it happen? When did specific events within the story happen? When was this passage written?

- **Where?** Where did it take place? Where did specific events within the story take place? Where was the author when he wrote this passage? Where were his readers?

- **Why?** Why did it happen? Why did people do what they did or say what they said? Why was the author writing this? Why does he give these instructions?

- **How?** How did it happen? How long did the events take to happen?

In the lesson for Day 1, we answered some of these questions related to the background of the book. Today we will answer questions about one specific section of 1 Peter.

Read 1 Peter 2:11-3:9.

A. Who is being addressed in this passage? We will mark with BLUE all references to the recipients of this letter. In verse 11, Peter refers to the recipients of his letter as **sojourners** or **foreigners**. He is speaking to Christians who are living on earth among unbelievers, but whose true citizenship is in heaven. Mark these words with BLUE. (The words may differ slightly, depending on the translation you are reading.)

After his general instructions to these readers, Peter gives specific directions to **three different groups** of people. Read the verses again. As you read, mark with BLUE the words that describe these three groups.

At the close of our passage, in 1 Peter 3:8-9, Peter finally addresses "all of you". Mark these words in BLUE also.

B. What does Peter tell each of these groups of people to do? Read the passage again. Mark with ORANGE the specific direction he gives to each group.

C. Why does Peter instruct them in this way? We use several different words to introduce reasons when we talk to people. The word **because** is probably the most common word we use when we are talking.

For example, in the sentence "I need to go to the store because we're all out of milk", the word **because** is followed by the reason for going to the store. What is the reason for going to the store in this sentence?

_____

In the Bible, several other words are used to introduce reasons. In addition to **because,** words like **for, so that,** and even just **that** by itself may introduce a reason for what has just been said or what is about to be said.

D. Read 1 Peter 2:11-3:9 again and mark with RED any of these words that introduce reasons for what Peter has directed his readers to do. Look for **because, for, so that,** and **that**. Remember, these words don't *always* introduce a reason. Read carefully, and mark the ones that do.

Your questions will be different, depending on the type of passage you are studying.

For example, if you are reading a narrative, such as a passage in the historical books of the Old Testament or in the gospels, you will answer questions related to the event that is being described.

If you are reading a New Testament epistle, you will be answering questions as they relate to the writer's instructions to his readers.

Day 3 - Organize observations

Use the chart below to organize your observations from Day 3. In the appropriate sections, list the people addressed (which you marked in BLUE), the directions given to them (which you marked in ORANGE), and the reasons for these directions (which will follow the words you marked in RED).

Person	Instruction	Reason

Day 4 - More observation

A. What is the main theme of this passage? What common theme do all of Peter's instructions share in this portion of the letter?

_____

B. Who does Peter point to as our example? _____

C. Observe what Peter says about Jesus:

What did Jesus do?

_____

_____

_____

_____

What did Jesus not do?

_____

_____

_____

_____

Why did Jesus act in this way? (You should be able to find more than one reason.)

_____

_____

_____

Day 5 - Interpret

A. Taking time to better understand some key words in this passage will help us apply the truths of this passage more effectively. Use a dictionary to define the following words:

Submit

_____

_____

Subjection

_____

_____

Honor

_____

_____

B. Compare these definitions to the information given about each word in Strong's Exhaustive Concordance (see sidebar).

Definitions from the Hebrew dictionary in _Strong's Concordance_:

1. Submit - _To subordinate, to obey, be under obedience, put under, submit self to._

2. Subjection - (This is another English translation of the exact same Hebrew word that is also translated as **submit**. It means the same thing as **submit**.)

3. Honor - _To prize, to fix a valuation upon, to revere, to value._

C. Review the passage and your notes in the chart from Day 3. List each person who is told to **submit** to someone else, and to whom they are to submit.

_____

_____

_____

D. Review the passage and chart from Day 3 again, this time listing each person who is instructed to **honor** someone, and who they are to honor.

_____

_____

_____

E. Which ones of these instructions from Questions C and D apply directly to you?

_____

_____

F. In what relationships could you apply the instructions given to servants?

_____

_____

G. ✳ In what relationships could you apply the instructions given to wives?

_____

_____

Day 6 - Interpret and apply

Words like **therefore**, **so**, and **likewise** are often clues that help us know how to interpret what we have been reading. They point back to what has already been said, and introduce instructions on how we should think or act because of what has been said. In this lesson we are going to look for those clues.

A. The word **likewise** means "in the same way". Read 1 Peter 2:11-3:9 again. Mark in GREEN every appearance of the words **likewise** (or **in the same way/in the same manner**, depending on the translation you're reading).

List below the verse where the word is found, who is being addressed, and the instructions they are given.

_____

_____

_____

Look carefully at the verses that precede these two appearances of **likewise**. What is **likewise** referring to? If these people are to submit "in the same manner", to whom or what is Peter pointing them as their example?

_____

B. ✳ How can you as a daughter **apply** to your relationship with your parents the instructions that are given to wives in this passage? (As you humbly submit to your parents now, you are learning how to humbly submit to the husband God may someday give you.)

_____

_____

C. Take a few minutes to prayerfully review your notes from Day 4, Question C. What can you learn from the example of Jesus that you can practice now while relating to your parents?

_____

_____

D. According to 1 Peter 3:3-4, what is the best way for a woman to adorn herself or make herself beautiful?

_____

_____

E. What, according to these verses, creates imperishable, unfading beauty?

_____

_____

We will spend more time studying these two verses in the next study.

Day 7 - Conclusion and application

A. Read 1 Peter 3:8-9.

What word does 1 Peter 3:8 begin with? _____

This word tells us that we are reaching the end of the discussion on a particular subject. Different groups of people have been addressed, and Peter is bringing this specific list of instructions to a close.

Who does Peter address in verses 8 and 9? _____

Application:

It's important that your application is both **specific** and **achievable**. A thought or feeling isn't true application unless you take action or make a noticeable change in your life. "I want to be more diligent" is a good goal, but if you make the specific goal, "I will get up at 6:30 and do my chores every day this week" you are more likely to grow in diligence.

For further study:

- Using the method described in Study 5 , study the following words and how they are used in other passages of the Bible:

  1. Submit

  2. Honor

  3. Suffer

  4. Revile

  5. Respectful (3:2)

- Study the life of Jesus, especially His last day leading up to the crucifixion. Note how He responded to those who wronged Him.

- Use Nave's Topical Bible to do a topical study of submission and obedience.

- Study the meaning of other words used in this passage, using a dictionary and a concordance as shown in Study 3.

What does Peter tell his readers to do?

_____

_____

What does he tell them to not do?

_____

_____

What should they do instead?

_____

_____

Why should they do this?

_____

_____

What will be the result?

_____

_____

B. ✷ Prayerfully review this entire study, starting with Day 1.

Summarize what you have learned.

_____

_____

_____

_____

Are there sins you need to repent of? With God's help, what will you do to change? Be specific.

_____

_____

_____

_____

Study 2

Beauty in the Heart

A Verse Study of 1 Peter 3:3-4

*"Whose adorning let it not be that outward adorning of plaiting the hair,
and of wearing of gold, or of putting on of apparel;
But let it be the hidden man of the heart, in that which is not corruptible,
even the ornament of a meek and quiet spirit, which is in the sight of God of great price."
(1 Peter 3:3-4)*

Now that we have studied the context of 1 Peter 3:3-4, let's spend more time studying these two verses and their description of imperishable beauty. We will read these verses in other translations, study key words in the verses, and think about their meaning and how to apply them in our lives.

Day 1 - Memorize

1 Peter 3:3-4 is one of the key passages we will be studying in this book. Memorizing it will help make it part of our thinking.

A. Memorize 1 Peter 3:3-4. Copy these verses from the translation of the Bible that you prefer to use when memorizing.

_____

_____

_____

_____

_____

_____

_____

_____

B. Copy the verses a second time onto a card or sticky note to carry in your purse or to post on your mirror or refrigerator for easy reference throughout the day. Keep reviewing the verses until you can recite both from memory.

Verse Study:

1. Memorize

2. Observe

3. Read related passages

4. Study key words

5. Apply

What you will need:

- Bible

- At least three additional Bibles in different translations

Day 2 - Observe

A. Read 1 Peter 3:3-4.

Draw an X over the **not** in verse 3, and circle in red the word *but* in verse 4. (In NIV circle the word *instead*, and in NKJV circle *rather*.) Verses 3 and 4 give us two contrasting commands – "Don't do this, but do this." They tell women what to not do, and then tell us what to do instead.

Two types of adorning are being contrasted. What are they?

_____

What does verse 3 say a woman should not rely on for her beauty?

_____

_____

_____

Instead, how should a woman adorn herself?

_____

_____

_____

B. Read these two verses in at least three other translations.

Are these verses saying that braided hair and jewelry and wearing clothes are bad?

_____

If not, then what are they saying?

_____

_____

_____

C. What two qualities are described as **not corruptible** (KJV), **incorruptible** (NKJV), **imperishable** (ESV and NASB), or **unfading** (NIV)?

_____

_____

Use a dictionary to define the word **corruptible**.

_____

_____

Use a dictionary to define the word **imperishable**.

_____

_____

_____

If verse 4 is describing a beauty that is not corruptible, what does this tell us about the contrasted external beauty in verse 3?

_____

_____

What is God's view of this internal, imperishable beauty?

_____

_____

_____

Day 3 - More verses

A. One practice that can help us understand a passage better is to read other verses in the Bible that use some of the same words. The same Greek word that is translated "not corruptible" in 1 Peter 3:3-4 is also used in many other places in the Bible. Read the following verses. What or who is being described as incorruptible in each verse? Record any additional observations.

Romans 1:23

_____

_____

1 Corinthians 9:25

_____

_____

1 Corinthians 15:52

_____

_____

1 Timothy 1:17

_____

_____

1 Peter 1:4

_____

_____

1 Peter 1:23

_____

_____

B. Based on what you have learned about the phrase **not corruptible** in these verses, summarize what you believe Peter means when he speaks of beauty that is not corruptible.

_____

_____

_____

_____

_____

Day 4 - Study words

In Day 3's lesson, we learned about the phrase "not corruptible" by reading other verses that contain the same Greek word. (We'll learn how to use *Strong's Concordance* to do this with other words in Study 5.)

We can also learn more about a word in the New Testament by looking up the original word in a Greek lexicon (dictionary), or by reading about the word in *Vine's Expository Dictionary of New Testament Words*. We will learn how to do this in more detail in Study 5. In our present study, the definitions and information from these resources will be provided for you.

We will look at several key words in 1 Peter 3:3-4.

A. Adorning

This passage speaks of a woman's adornment. The Greek word used for adornment is **kosmos**. The only time in the New Testament that this Greek word is translated as **adornment** is in 1 Peter 3:3. In every other verse where the word is used, it is translated as world. It speaks of a **harmonious arrangement** or order, such as the order and harmony that God established when He created the world.

The verb form of this word is applied to the **furnishing of a room**. It is also used in verse 5 of 1 Peter 3, speaking of how holy women of old, those whose hope was in God, adorned themselves by submitting to their own husbands. These ladies brought order and harmony to their souls and beautified themselves, by trusting God and demonstrating that trust by submitting to their husbands.

List different relationships you have with others, and how you demonstrate your trust in God in those relationships. Be specific.

_____

_____

_____

_____

_____

_____

Do some of your relationships reveal your lack of trust in God? What will you do to change this?

_____

_____

_____

_____

_____

B. ✳ Outward and hidden

These two ways of adorning ourselves are contrasted in 1 Peter 3:3-4. We should not focus on the **external adorning** of ourselves, but on the adorning that is **concealed or private**.

It's easy for us ladies to become preoccupied with what people can easily see from the outside. It's not wrong to adorn ourselves outwardly. Our outer appearance is part of how we reflect God's glory. But if we rely on outward adornment and neglect our souls, we will not be truly beautiful. Our inner beauty is what is precious in God's sight, and it is reflected in our outward appearance.

What sorts of things do you do to adorn yourself outwardly?

_____

_____

_____

_____

_____

What do you do to adorn yourself inwardly?

_____

_____

_____

_____

_____

_____

_____

_____

C. Heart

The Greek word for heart in these verses is **kardia**. This is the same word from which we get words like cardiologist, cardiac arrest, and electrocardiogram. It can refer to the literal organ that pumps blood all through your body. But is also speaks about our soul.

Vine's Expository Dictionary of New Testament Words says this about **kardia:**

> *"The heart, the chief organ of physical life, occupies the most important place in the human system. By an easy transition the word came to stand for man's entire mental and moral activity, both the rational and the emotional elements. In other words, the heart is used figuratively for the hidden springs of the personal life."*

Thayer's Greek-English Lexicon of the Old Testament adds additional insight into this word:

> *"The center and seat of spiritual life, the soul or mind, as it is the fountain and seat of the thoughts, passions, desires, appetites, affections, purposes, endeavors."*

Based on this information, what do you think Peter means when he speaks of the "hidden person of the heart"?

_____

_____

_____

Day 5 - More word study

Peter identifies two qualities of imperishable beauty. These two qualities are often misunderstood and wrongly defined. We will study those in detail today.

A. Meek

Carefully read what *Vine's Expository Dictionary of New Testament Words* has to say about **meekness**:

> "…It is an inwrought grace of the soul; and the exercises of it are first and chiefly towards God. It is that temper of spirit in which we accept His dealings with us as good, and therefore without disputing or resisting."

> "…This meekness, however, being first of all a meekness before God, is also such in the face of men, even of evil men, out of a sense that these, with the insults and injuries which they may inflict, are permitted and employed by Him for the chastening and purifying of His elect."

> "The meaning of prautes is not readily expressed in English, for the terms meekness, mildness, commonly used, suggest weakness and pusillanimity (timidity or cowardliness) to a greater or less extent, whereas prautes does nothing of this kind…It must be understood, therefore, that the meekness manifested by the Lord and commended to the believer is the fruit of power. The common assumption is that when a man is meek it is because he cannot help himself; but the Lord was 'meek' because He had the infinite resources of God at His command. Described negatively, meekness is the opposite of self-assertiveness and self-interest… "

Is a meek person a weak person?

_____

According to these quotes from *Vine's*, what is meekness the fruit of?

_____

In whose power does the meek person trust?

_____

What is the opposite of meekness?

_____

Two men are specifically identified as meek in Scripture. Who are they?

Numbers 12:3

_____

Matthew 11:29

_____

Summarize what the following verses tell us about Jesus:

Isaiah 53:7

_____

_____

Strong's Concordance:

Strong's Exhaustive Concordance was compiled by James Strong, a Methodist Bible scholar in the late 1800's. Dr. Strong was not a pastor, but he served as Professor of Exegetical Theology at Drew Theological Seminary (now Drew University) in Madison, New Jersey. He was one of five men who formed the core faculty of this seminary from its inception in 1867. He traveled in Europe, Israel, and Egypt while doing research for another theological work. He served as mayor of his hometown and built his own railroad company. He was known for his pursuit of excellence, and he was an enthusiastic and respected teacher. A Dr. Buckley said of him,

"At night in his library, he worked like a plow-horse, but in the lecture room he was as frisky as a colt. No one ever went to sleep in his classes unless he was out of health or an imbecile."

Dr. Strong could see the value that an exhaustive concordance would be to Bible scholars, in a day when no such reference tool existed. He worked for thirty-five years to catalog and organize every single word used in the King James version of the Bible into a complete concordance, assigning numbers to the original Hebrew and Greek words and creating a dictionary of these words as well. The work was finally published in 1890, just four years before he died. Today, computers make this job much easier, but he did all the work by hand.

Matthew 26:47-54

_____

_____

In Study 1 we looked at 1 Peter 2:11-3:9. Peter summarizes this portion of his letter with an exhortation to meekness. What does he say our response should be when we are wronged by others (see 1 Peter 3:9)?

_____

_____

_____

Based on what you have learned about meekness in this study, describe how a meek person responds to troublesome circumstances and people.

_____

_____

_____

_____

_____

B. Quiet

Strong's Exhaustive Concordance defines **quiet** as "keeping one's seat" and as "still, undisturbed, and undisturbing".

Vine's Expository Dictionary of New Testament Words describes it as "a tranquility arising from within, causing no disturbance to others".

Strong's defines the verb form of this word as "refrain from labor, meddle-someness or speech".

Read the following verses and note what they say about **quietness**:

1 Timothy 2:2

_____

_____

1 Thessalonians 4:11

_____

_____

Is a Christian woman or young lady who displays this quiet quality of spirit required to be shy and timid?

_____

_____

Summarize what you have learned about **quiet** as it is used in 1 Peter 3:4.

_____

_____

_____

_____

Day 6 - Application

A. Matthew Henry, in his *Commentary on the Whole Bible*, says this about 1 Peter 3:3-4:

> *"It must, in general, be something not corruptible that beautifies the soul, that is, the graces and virtues of God's Holy Spirit. The ornaments of the body are destroyed by the moth, and perish in the using; but the grace of God, the longer we wear it, the brighter and better it is. More especially, the finest ornament of Christian women is a meek and quiet spirit, a tractable easy temper of mind, void of passion, pride, and immoderate anger, discovering itself in a quiet obliging behaviour towards their husbands and families."*

Rewrite this quote in your own words.

_____

_____

_____

_____

_____

_____

_____

_____

_____

_____

For additional study:

• Using the method described in Study 5, study the words **meek**, **quiet**, and **chaste** and their use in Scripture:

• Use this verse study method to further study 1 Peter 3:5-6.

• Read at least two commentaries on 1 Peter 3:3-4 and summarize what you learn.

• Read and study the comments on 1 Peter 3:1-7 in *Matthew Henry's Commentary*. What can you take from these comments to apply to your present relationship with your parents?

• Study the life of Moses, the man who was "very meek, above all the men which were upon the face of the earth". (Num.12:3) Use the method outlined in Study 3. Note the evidences of Moses's meekness in his interactions with God, with his father-in-law, and with the Israelites.

• In Matthew 11:29, Jesus tells us, "Take my yoke upon you, and learn of me; for I am meek and lowly in heart: and ye shall find rest unto your souls." Study the life of Jesus. How was his meekness demonstrated?

• What promises are given to the meek? Use your concordance and topical Bible to answer this question. Make a list of all the promises.

• Study Genesis 24:53, Psalm 45:8-14, Proverbs 31:22, and Ezekiel 16:10-17. What can we learn from these passages? Does God disapprove of outward adornment?

Is your life characterized by the qualities Matthew Henry lists as evidences of a meek and quiet spirit? In what areas do you need to grow?

_____

_____

_____

_____

_____

_____

B. ✱ Reread 1 Peter 3:1-6 to recall the context of verses 3 and 4.

How do you think a wife should apply Peter's instructions in verses 3 and 4?

_____

_____

_____

_____

How can you, as a daughter, apply the principles of these instructions to your relationship with your parents?

_____

_____

_____

_____

_____

_____

C. Repent to God and to others you have sinned against through a lack of the meek and quiet spirit that God values so much. Then prayerfully commit, with the Holy Spirit's enabling, to "putting on" meekness.

Study 3

Beauty in Trusting God

A Character Study of Sarah

"...as Sarah obeyed Abraham, calling him lord. And you are her children, if you do good and do not fear anything that is frightening." (1 Peter 3:6, ESV)

In 1 Peter 3, Sarah is held up to us as an example of godly beauty. We know from the Old Testament that even in her old age, she was so beautiful that her husband knew she would attract the attention of kings in the foreign lands they traveled through. She is also praised in the New Testament as an example of fearless submission and God-honoring faith.

In this study we will learn the basic steps of a character study as we look at Sarah's life.

Character study:

1. Find and read person's story in the Bible
2. Use study helps to find background information
3. Note observations
4. Study difficult passages
5. Summarize & apply

What you will need:

- Bible
- Concordance
- Bible atlas
- Bible dictionary or commentary

Day 1 - Read Sarah's story in the Bible

A. ✻ Use *Strong's Exhaustive Concordance* (or an online concordance, see page 46) to compile a list of every reference to Sarah. Look up the word **Sarah** in the concordance and record each reference listed. Do the same for the word **Sarai**, her name before it was changed to Sarah.

____

____

____

____

____

____

____

B. The main account of Sarah's life is recorded in the book of Genesis. Rather than reading isolated verses from Genesis about her, read the entire story of Abraham and Sarah. Start in the first chapter she is mentioned and read continuously until you reach the last reference to her. You will get a much fuller picture of her life this way, and better understand her life with Abraham and the others around her.

Divide the verses into two sections, and read one portion today and the other portion tomorrow. Answer the following questions as you read:

Look up Sarah in a Bible dictionary online:

1. Go to www.biblestudytools.com.

2. Click on "Library" in the upper tool bar.

3. Click on "Dictionaries".

4. In the "Search dictionaries" box, type "Sarah," and hit enter.

5. You'll find entries in several Bible dictionaries explaining the meaning of her name, where she is mentioned in Scripture, etc.

Finding Bible maps online:

- At www.biblemap.org, you can enter book and chapter of the Bible that you are reading, and it will pinpoint any locations on the map for you.

- Go to http://www.biblestudy.org/maps/main.html. Scroll down and view the two maps entitled "Palestine during the Biblical patriarchs" and "Abraham's Journey to Land of Canaan".

- At www.bible.ca/maps/, scroll down the page and you will find several maps related to Abraham.

Sarai's name was changed to Sarah. What do both names mean?

_____

_____

What was her family ancestry?

_____

_____

What was her husband's family ancestry?

_____

_____

Day 2 - Continue reading

Where did Sarah live and where did she travel to? (Find these places in a Bible atlas.)

_____

_____

_____

_____

When did she live? (Use a Bible dictionary or commentary to help you answer this question.)

_____

_____

_____

What were the main events in her life?

_____

_____

_____

_____

_____

Day 3 - Additional details

Read through the verses about Sarah again and look for answers to the following questions:

At what times did Sarah submit to her husband?

_____

_____

_____

_____

_____

_____

What promises were made to her husband Abraham?

_____

_____

_____

_____

_____

_____

When was her beauty noticed and admired? How old was she at these times?

_____

_____

_____

_____

What hardships did she endure?

_____

_____

_____

_____

_____

What temptations did she face?

_____

_____

_____

_____

_____

_____

What evidences do you notice of her faith in God?

_____

_____

_____

_____

_____

What apparent mistakes did she make and what were the results?

_____

_____

_____

_____

_____

What is she remembered for in the New Testament?

_____

_____

_____

Day 4 - Questions

A. Read Gen. 12:10-20 again. Abraham is often seen as being cowardly in this account. Answer the following questions:

Considering her beauty and the attention she had already attracted, what might have happened to Sarah if the Egyptians killed Abraham?

_____

_____

Reread verses 12 and 13. If you have access to an ESV Bible (you can also look online), read this verse again in that translation. Do you think Abraham might have been trying to protect Sarah by posing as her brother?

_____

_____

Read Gen. 20:12. Was Abraham actually her brother?

_____

Do you think Abraham was forgetting that God was able to protect him and his wife?

_____

How did God protect Sarah when she was in the household of Pharaoh?

_____

_____

_____

B. Read all of Genesis 20 again and compare it with the account in Genesis 12.

What details are the same in this story?

_____

_____

_____

_____

_____

What details are different?

_____

_____

_____

_____

_____

How did God protect Sarah in this situation?

_____

_____

What else does God do in this account?

_____

_____

_____

Reread verses 11-13. How did Abraham answer when Abimelech asked what he saw that led him to act in the way he did?

_____

_____

_____

How did Sarah respond in both Genesis 12 and Genesis 20?

_____

_____

_____

Day 5 - More questions

A. Read Genesis 16 again. This is another story in Sarah's life that is a bit confusing.

Summarize what Sarah suggested to Abraham.

_____

_____

Sarah was suggesting that Hagar bear a child on her behalf. Because she was barren, Hagar would bear a child for her, and the child would become Abraham's heir. This was a custom of that day. Why do you think Sarah did this? Do you think Sarah knew the promises that God had made to Abraham?

_____

_____

What were the results of this decision?

_____

_____

_____

According to God's promise to Hagar (verses 11-12), what will Ishmael and his descendants be like?

_____

_____

How was Hagar to respond to Sarah's treatment, according to God's words to her after she had fled from Sarah?

_____

_____

Use a Bible dictionary to learn more about the Ishmaelites, the descendants of Hagar's son.

_____

_____

_____

Do you think Sarah's idea of bearing a child through Hagar was a good one? Why?

_____

_____

B. Note below any other questions you have about Sarah's life and the references of any specific passages you found puzzling. Leave space after each question or reference to record answers that you find.

_____

_____

_____

_____

_____

_____

Use a commentary, Bible dictionary or study Bible to look for answers to these questions. Ask your parents and pastor for their insights.

> "'Wife' is here used to describe an inferior, though not degrading, relation, in countries where polygamy prevails. In the case of these female slaves, who are the personal property of his lady, being purchased before her marriage or given as a special present to her, no one can become the husband's secondary wife without her mistress' consent or permission. This usage seems to have prevailed in patriarchal times; and Hagar, Sarai's slave, of whom she had the entire right of disposing, was given by her mistress' spontaneous offer, to be the secondary wife of Abram, in the hope of obtaining the long-looked-for heir. It was a wrong step–indicating a want of simple reliance on God–and Sarai was the first to reap the bitter fruits of her device."
>
> – Robert Jamieson, Jamieson, Fausset & Brown Commentary

Day 6 - New Testament references

A. Read 1 Peter 3:1-6.

Reread verse 4. We talked about imperishable beauty in Study 2. Do you think Sarah had the imperishable beauty of a meek and gentle spirit? If so, could this be part of why Sarah was still so beautiful, even at the age of 65, that Abraham was worried that he might be killed by those who were attracted to her?

_____

How, according to this passage, did holy women of God adorn themselves?

_____

_____

_____

Reread verse 6. You have read all the passages in the Bible that tell us about Sarah. Does Scripture record her actually "calling him lord"? List examples of Sarah's submission to Abraham.

_____

_____

_____

_____

_____

According to the last part of 1 Peter 3:6, how do we become Sarah's "children"?

_____

_____

Think back over all that you have learned about Sarah. Review the passages that tell her story. Then list the different times in her life with Abraham when she would have been tempted to be afraid.

_____

_____

_____

_____

_____

B. Read Hebrews 11:8-16.

What were the evidences of faith in Abraham's life?

_____

_____

_____

_____

Do you think these circumstances would have been a test of his wife's faith, as well as his?

_____

What did Sarah receive as a result of her faith?

_____

_____

_____

Did Abraham and Sarah see the entire fulfillment of God's promises to them before they died?

_____

Did they still believe God would keep His promises?

_____

Day 7 - Summary and application

A. Write a short summary of Sarah's life.

_____

_____

_____

_____

_____

_____

_____

_____

_____

For further study:

• Many other men and women are given to us as examples of faith. Using the method described in Study 8, study the entire chapter of Hebrews 11. What is faith? How did these people prove their faith in God? What can you learn from them?

• 1 Peter 3:6 says that we are Sarah's daughters when we choose to obey and "are not afraid with any amazement". Use your concordance to study Scripture passages that tell us to "fear not". What do you learn from these passages that will help you obey with courage like Sarah did?

• Using the method outlined in Study 6, do a topical study of **trust**. What do you learn that will help you trust and obey God in all the circumstances of your life?

• Make a list of all God's promises as you read through the entire Bible. (You can also mark these in a special way in your Bible.) Note each reference and promise, and categorize these promises in a form that you can review them when you need encouragement to trust God in all things.

• Study the topic of **lying** in the Bible. Is it ever right to lie? What verses and stories in the Bible support your conclusion?

List several words to describe Sarah's character:

_____

_____

B. What lessons can you learn from Sarah's life?

_____

_____

_____

_____

In what areas are you tempted to be afraid?

_____

_____

_____

What do you need to remember in order to overcome your fears?

_____

_____

_____

In what areas is God calling you to trust Him more fully?

_____

_____

_____

_____

What will you do differently?

_____

_____

_____

_____

Beauty in Humility

A Book Study on the Book of Esther

"For Esther did the commandment of Mordecai, like as when she was brought up with him."
(Esther 2:20b)

Esther was a beautiful woman – the most beautiful in all the Persian Empire, according to King Ahasuerus's opinion. The writer of the book of Esther agrees. Esther 2:7 says, in part, "…and the maid was fair and beautiful". What can we learn about beauty from the most beautiful lady in the Persian Empire?

In the book of Esther we are privileged to observe a beautiful woman whose attitudes and actions exhibit the meek and quiet spirit that God values so much.

Unlike the beautiful woman without discretion that Proverbs 11:22 speaks of, Esther was incredibly patient and perceptive as she worked to save her people. She understood authority and human nature and appealed to the king in a wise and courageous way.

Like Sarah, Esther was a woman with a strong-but-meek spirit. The book of Esther is unique in that it makes no specific mention of God, but Esther must have had a strong and deep faith that trusted in God's control of all circumstances. Even as the queen of Persia, her humility and respect for authority are apparent in her responses to Mordecai and to King Ahasuerus.

We can learn much about godly womanhood and beauty as we study this courageous lady's life. And while we study her, we will also learn how to study an entire book of the Bible. (We will focus primarily on the first eight chapters.)

We will be marking different words in the text as we read. **If you don't want to mark in your Bible, use a computer to print out the entire book of Esther**. Print it in a larger font and leave space between lines, if possible.

Day 1 - Background

Use a study Bible, commentary, or Bible dictionary to learn more about the book of Esther.

Who is its author?

_____

Book study:

1. Research background

2. Read the book

3. Summarize narrative

4. Highlight and study main characters

5. Create a timeline

6. Assign titles to chapters

7. Analyze main character(s)

8. Review and summarize

9. Apply

What you will need:

- Bible

- Printout of the text of Esther, if you don't want to mark in your Bible

- Study Bible or commentary

- Colored pencils

When was it written?

_____

What other books of the Bible took place during the same time period as Esther?

_____

_____

_____

Where were the Jews during this time period?

_____

_____

What literary style is it written in?

_____

Day 2 - Summarize

Read the entire book of Esther, and summarize the story.

_____

_____

_____

_____

_____

_____

_____

Literary styles in the Bible :

- Narratives
- Laws
- Poetry
- Proverbs
- Genealogies
- Prophecy
- Letters

Day 3 - Highlight the main characters

Read chapters 1-5 of Esther. As you read mark the following words:

A. Highlight **Esther** and pronouns referring to her with PURPLE. Underline her **actions** and **words** with purple. (What did she do? What did she say?)

B. Highlight **Ahasuerus** and pronouns referring to him with ORANGE. Underline his actions and words with orange.

C. Circle **Haman's** name and pronouns referring to him with BLACK. Underline his actions and words with black.

D. Mark **Mordecai** and his pronouns with BLUE. Underline his actions and words with blue.

E. Other people will be mentioned in these chapters. Decide how you would like to mark their names, actions, and words, and use those markings throughout these chapters and again when you finish reading the book in the next lesson.

Day 4 - Continue reading

Read chapters 6-10 of Esther. As you read, continue to mark the names of different people with the same markings that you used in the previous lesson.

Day 5 - Actions

Look back over your markings and list the **main actions** of each character in the story.

Esther

_____

_____

_____

_____

_____

_____

_____

_____

_____

King Ahasuerus

_____

_____

_____

_____

_____

_____

_____

The **law of the Medes and Persians** could not be withdrawn. Once a law was made, it was unalterable. When Darius made a law that no one could pray to anyone but him, he could not change that law when Daniel became a victim to his enemies' plot against him. When Ahasuerus gave Haman his signet ring and approved his plan to annihilate the Jews, that law could not be revoked. After Haman's execution, in order to deal with this law, Ahasuerus gave Esther and Mordecai authority to write another law that granted the Jews permission to defend themselves.

_____

_____

_____

Mordecai

_____

_____

_____

_____

_____

_____

Haman

_____

_____

_____

_____

_____

_____

_____

_____

_____

Other secondary characters

_____

_____

_____

_____

_____

_____

_____

_____

_____

_____

_____

Based on what you have read and noted, write a one-line description for the character of these four main people in the story.

Esther_____

King Ahasuerus _____

Haman _____

Mordecai _____

Day 6 - Related verses

A. Read the following Proverbs. How does each relate to the story of Haman's life?

Proverbs 11:2

_____

_____

Proverbs 16:18

_____

_____

Proverbs 20:2

_____

_____

B. Read the following Proverbs. Explain how each relates to King Ahasuerus's decisions and actions:

Proverbs 15:22

_____

_____

Proverbs 16:13

_____

_____

Proverbs 21:1

_____

_____

C. Read the following Proverbs, and tell how each relates to Esther's life:

Proverbs 13:16

_____

_____

Proverbs 16:21

_____

_____

Proverbs 22:11

_____

_____

Day 7 - Time and location

Read chapters 1-5 again. This time we will be watching for two different things – times and locations.

A. Draw a RED box around every mention of time (times of day, words like "later", "after these things", "when such-and-such happened", "in the days of", etc.).

B. Draw a BROWN box around every mention of location (names of countries, provinces, and cities; places within the city or palace, etc.).

Day 8 - Time and location (continued)

Read chapters 6-10 again and continue marking times in RED and locations in BROWN.

When you have finished, record significant observations about **time** and **locations** in this story.

_____

_____

_____

_____

_____

_____

_____

Day 9 - Timeline

A. Record the main events of Esther in chronological order, noting specific times when they are given in the text.

_____

_____

_____

_____

_____

_____

_____

_____

_____

_____

_____

_____

_____

_____

_____

_____

B. Note any new observations you have made after compiling this timeline.

_____

_____

_____

_____

_____

Day 10 - Chapter titles

Skim the entire book of Esther again. Assign a title to each chapter – a short group of words that summarizes the main events or thoughts of the chapter. Write your titles in the chart below.

We are also going to take a closer look at Esther's character, since she is the example of beauty and discretion that we are focusing on this study. We have already summarized her character, but this time, as you read each chapter and assign titles to them, take time to select one or two words that describe Esther's character as it is displayed in the events of that chapter. Was she brave? Prudent? Obedient? Write your descriptive words next to your chapter titles below.

Chapter: Title: Description of Esther:

1 _____ .

2 _____

3 _____

4 _____

5 _____

6 _____

7 _____

8 _____

9 _____

10 _____ (not present in this chapter) _____

Day 11 - Esther's Relationships to other People in the Story

Carefully reread chapters 1-5 of Esther, paying special attention to how Esther relates to the other characters of the story, and how they respond to her. Watch for repeated words and repeated actions that might help you in your observations. (You will continue this chart for chapters 6-10 in Day 12's assignment.)

	Esther toward person(s)	*Person(s) toward Esther*
Mordecai		
Hegai		
Maidens and Eunuchs		
King Ahasuerus		
Haman		

Day 12 - Finish analyzing Esther's relationships

Continue reading chapters 6-10 while noting Esther's interactions with other people.

Day 13 - Review

Review your notes from Days 5-10. Think about how all these different factors relate to each other and lead to the story's conclusion.

• The character of different people
• The actions of different people
• The sequence of events
• Esther's interactions with others

Even though God is not specifically mentioned in the book of Esther, His presence and sovereign control are obvious. Describe, using all the factors listed above, how God intervened to preserve His people. (With a few changes in the details of the story, things could have ended quite differently.)

_____

_____

_____

_____

_____

_____

_____

Day 14 - Application

✱ Esther was a beautiful and courageous woman. In this account of her life, we can see the evidences of a meek spirit that trusted God and humbly submitted to His ordained authorities. We see her patiently appeal to the king with respect and discretion. We can see how Esther understood the character of others, and how she wisely used the opportunities, position, and talents that God granted her in order to serve others and even save their lives. These are traits of a godly and truly beautiful woman.

In what areas can you be more like Esther? What qualities can you imitate? Are you facing any situations where you could exercise godly discretion like Esther did? What specific lessons can you learn from her life?

_____

_____

_____

_____

_____

_____

_____

_____

_____

_____

_____

_____

_____

_____

_____

For additional study:

- Read Esther aloud with your family. Assign people to read specific parts: narrator, Esther, Morde-cai, Haman, Ahasuerus, the king's wise men and attendants.

- Read Esther again, with your father reading aloud. Following the tradition of the Jewish Purim, arm the rest of the family with vari-ous noisemakers – pots and pans and spoons, whistles, etc. Every time Haman's name is read, blot it out with your noisemakers.

- Study all the details of Esther's appeal to King Ahasuerus. Make a time-line of all the details. Note everything she said and how she said it. Apply what you learn to situa-tions where you need to appeal to an authority.

- Contrast the lives of Ha-man and Mordecai. What can you learn from the example of both of these men?

- Note all the feasts in the book of Esther. Mark each mention of a feast through-out the text, and then list them. Is there any special significance apparent in the many feasts listed?

- Note the use of the word "favor" in the book of Esther. Mark the word each time it is mentioned in the text. Using the word study method outlined in Study 5, find out what original Hebrew word(s) were used in these pas-sages. Is it the same word that is used in Proverbs 31:30, which states that "favor is deceitful?" Study other uses of the word "favor" throughout Scripture.

Study 5

Beauty in Modesty

A Verse Study of 1 Timothy 2:9-10

"In like manner also, that women adorn themselves in modest apparel, with shamefacedness and sobriety; not with broided hair, or gold, or pearls, or costly array; but (which becometh women professing godliness) with good works." (1 Timothy 2:9-10)

Godly beauty is not passive. It is a condition of the soul that quietly, diligently expresses itself through actions! In this study we will examine what God says about a godly woman's true adornment. On what does a woman's true beauty depend?

In this study we will learn how to use *Strong's Exhaustive Concordance* to find verses that use specific words, and how to use the dictionaries at the back of the concordance to study the original Hebrew or Greek words and their meanings. This study walks you step-by-step through this process, but will take some time to complete. It's worth it! Once you learn how to do this, the process is fairly easy, and it's exciting to dig into the treasure of God's Word this way.

(If you have access to a computer or electronic device such as a tablet or smartphone – and can use it in your Bible study without becoming distracted by email, chat, and the internet – you can streamline this process quite a bit. Look for instructions in the sidebars.)

Day 1 - Background

A. Read the entire book of 1 Timothy. This will help you understand the context of verses 9 and 10 in chapter 2.

B. Answer the following questions, using a study Bible or commentary for help with those you can't answer directly from the text.

What is the literary style of this book?_____

Who wrote 1 Timothy? _____

Who is it written to? _____

What was the relationship between the author and recipient of this book?

_____

_____

_____

Verse study:

1. Read verse(s) in context

2. Observations

3. Other translations

4. Study key words

5. Conclusion and application

What you will need:

- Bible

- Four other Bible translations (in print or online)

- Strong's Concordance

A **lexicon** is a book containing an alphabetical arrangement of the words in a language and their definitions, or the vocabulary of a language, an individual speaker or group of speakers, or a subject.

Transliteration is the changing of letters and words into corresponding characters of another alphabet or language. The Hebrew and Greek dictionary in Strong's transliterate the original words of the Bible into letters of the English language.

Etymology is the study of the history, development, and origin of words.

What was the author's purpose in writing this book?

_____

_____

_____

What are the main themes of this book?

_____

_____

What subject is being addressed in chapter 2?

_____

We need to keep this in mind as we study verses 9 and 10.

Day 2 - Observation

A. Read 1 Timothy 2:9-10.

The author lists four different things a godly woman should *not* adorn herself with. Highlight those words with BLUE in the text and list them below:

_____

_____

_____

_____

How does this list compare with Peter's list in 1 Peter 3:3-4?

_____

_____

_____

B. Read Isaiah 3:16-23.

What does God say the attitude of the women described in this passage was?

_____

_____

What were they relying on for their adornment?

_____

_____

_____

_____

_____

_____

_____

What did God say was going to happen to these women when He judged Jerusalem?

_____

_____

C. Read 1 Timothy 2:9-10 again. Highlight with GREEN all the words that describe how a woman *should* seek to adorn or beautify herself.

What should a woman who professes godliness wear?

_____

With what attitude should she wear this?

_____

With what should the godly woman adorn herself?

_____

Day 3 - Other translations

Before we start to use *Strong's* to study the words in 1 Timothy 2:9-10, take the time to read these verses in at least four other translations of the Bible. (If you don't own other translations, follow the instructions in the sidebar for looking up other translations online.)

Note any new insights from your reading.

_____

_____

_____

_____

_____

_____

Compare Bible translations with an online parallel Bible:

To quickly compare different Bible translations of a verse, you can use an *online Parallel Bible.* This will help you see how different scholars translated the original Hebrew or Greek words into English, which will give you a better understanding of the key words in this verse.

1. Go to www.biblestudytools.com.

2. Click on "Bible Study" in the upper menu bar.

3. Click on "Parallel Bible".

4. Click on the cream-colored box labeled "Compare Translations". (It's near the middle of the screen.)

5. Scroll down to 1 Timothy, then to (chapter) 2, and then to (verse) 9.

6. When you click on the verse number, it will bring up the verse in a *bunch* of different translations.

7. Skimming through these will give you a little better understanding of the words, as you see the various ways the original Hebrew text has been translated.

8. As an *extra bonus,* the website also includes (at the bottom of all the translations) helpful notes from several Bible commentaries.

Day 4 - Strong's Concordance

Studying some of the main words in 1 Timothy 2:9-10 will help us better understand the verse. *Strong's Exhaustive Concordance* will help us with that study. Because *Strong's* is a complete listing of every word in the King James Version of the Bible, we will be looking up words as they appear in that translation.

Today we will learn how to use *Strong's* while we study the word **adorn**. When you look up **adorn**, you will see a listing that looks like the one below.

> **ADORN**
> 1Ti 2: 9 In like manner also, that women **a**   *G2885*
> Tit   2:10 that they may **a** the doctrine of God   *G2885*

Let's look at each portion of this listing. (To help you see the question portions of this study, a ❏ appears next to each section that asks for a written response. Each time you see a box, you will need to mark the text in some way or supply an answer to a question.)

A. References: The abbreviation and numbers at the beginning of each line indicate the reference of each verse in which the word **adorn** is used. If you are unfamiliar with standard abbreviations for the books of the Bible, refer to the list of abbreviations provided at the beginning of the concordance.

❏ In what book of the Bible will we find the first verse that is listed in this concordance entry? _____

B. Verse quotations: The words in the center of each line quote the portion of the verse that contains the word **adorn**.

> **ADORN**
> 1Ti 2: 9 In like manner also, that women **a**   *G2885*
> Tit   2:10 that they may **a** the doctrine of God   *G2885*

The "**a**" in each quote stands for the word **adorn**.

❏ What is the complete reference for the first verse listed? _____

This is the verse we are studying.

C. *Strong's* numbers: The numbers listed at the end of each line are numbers that correspond to definition numbers at the back of *Strong's*.

> **ADORN**
> 1Ti 2: 9 In like manner also, that women **a**   *G2885*
> Tit   2:10 that they may **a** the doctrine of God   *G2885*

❏ What number is assigned to the word **adorn** in this verse? _____

D. Original language: Numbers for references from the Old Testament are listed in standard type and indicate that these words will be listed in

Look up a word in Strong's Concordance online:

1. Go to www.biblestudytools.com.

2. Click on "Library" in the upper tool bar.

3. Click on "Concordances".

4. Click on "Strong's Exhaustive Concordance".

5. Type in "adorn" in the "Search the Bible with Strong's" box and click "Search".

the **Hebrew** portion of the dictionary (or **lexicon**). This dictionary appears first at the back of *Strong's*.

Numbers for references from the New Testament are listed in italic and point us to definitions in the **Greek** dictionary at the back of Strong's. This dictionary follows after the Hebrew one.

All Old Testament words will be defined in the Hebrew dictionary. All New Testament words will be defined in the Greek dictionary. The differences in type style will help you remember this.

ADORN
1Ti   2: 9 In like manner also, that women **a**   *G2885*
Tit   2:10 that they may **a** the doctrine of God   *G2885*

❏ Which lexicon will you use to look up the information about Number 2885 as it is used in the verse from 1 Timothy?

_____

E. What is the next verse listed under the word **adorn** in Strong's?

_____

F. What number is assigned to this verse? _____

G. Read this verse. What does it say? What do you learn about the word adorn in the verse?

_____

_____

H. To fully understand this verse, you should also read the verses that precede and follow it. These verses are called the **context**. Have you ever overheard just one sentence in someone else's conversation and jumped to the wrong conclusion about what was being said? The same thing can happen if we read isolated verses from the Bible without understanding their context. The context helps clarify the meaning of a verse.

The verse you just read in Question G starts in the middle of a thought. We need to read the context to know what Paul is saying.

Go back and read the verse that precedes it.

Who is being addressed in these verses? _____

In what way can this group of people "adorn the doctrine of God our Saviour in all things"? (If you are reading in the King James Version, you may need to look up the meaning of a word or two.)

_____

_____

_____

Look up original Hebrew or Greek words online:

1. Go to www.blueletter-bible.com

2. Type "1 Tim. 2:9" in the search box and click. This will bring up the entire chapter of 1 Timothy 2.

3. Make sure the "Show Strong's" box at the top of this chapter, on the right, is checked. This will cause blue numbers to show throughout the text.

4. Scroll down to verse 9 and click on the blue number that follows the word "adorn". This will open a lexicon entry for the Greek word that was translated as "adorn" in this verse.

In this listing you can see:

• The Greek word written in Greek

• The transliteration of the word into English

• The standard phonetic pronunciation markings for the word (along with an audio pronunciation)

• What part of speech the word is

• The etymology of the word

• What the word means as it is used in Scripture

• How many times the Greek word is used in the Bible and how it is translated

• Text from Thayer's Lexicon, written in the 1800's.

• Text of all the verses in the Bible that include the same Greek word that is used in 1 Timothy 2:9

Day 5 - Use the Greek dictionary to study a word

Today we will learn how to use the Strong's numbers to study a word and its meaning.

A. Turn to the Greek dictionary at the back of your concordance. (The pages will say "Greek Dictionary of the New Testament" on the top when you have found the right section of the book.)

Find No. 2885. (This was the number assigned to **adorn** in the verses we are studying.) You will see this entry:

> *G2885* κοσμέω *kosmeō* from *G2889*; to *put in* proper *order,* i.e. *decorate* (literally or figuratively); specifically to *snuff* (a wick):— adorn, garnish, trim.

B. Original Greek word: The first thing you see after the Strong's number is the original Greek word as it is written in Greek.

❑ Circle or highlight this word.

> *G2885* κοσμέω *kosmeō* from *G2889*; to *put in* proper *order,* i.e. *decorate* (literally or figuratively); specifically to *snuff* (a wick):— adorn, garnish, trim.

C. English equivalent or transliteration: Immediately following is the exact equivalent of the word in English letters. Standard English pronunciation markings help us know the precise pronunciation of the Greek words.

❑ Circle or highlight this word.

> *G2885* κοσμέω *kosmeō* from *G2889*; to *put in* proper *order,* i.e. *decorate* (literally or figuratively); specifically to *snuff* (a wick):— adorn, garnish, trim.

D. Word history: After the pronunciation, the **etymology** of the word is given. This is the history of the word, tracing it back to its root word or words. In this case, we are referred to No. 2889, the word **kosmos**. This information is useful because learning more about root words can often give a fuller understanding of the word being studied.

❑ Circle or highlight this listing.

> *G2885* κοσμέω *kosmeō* from *G2889*; to *put in* proper *order,* i.e. *decorate* (literally or figuratively); specifically to *snuff* (a wick):— adorn, garnish, trim.

E. Definition: Following the word's etymology is the concise meaning of the word. This portion of the dictionary entry ends with a colon (:).

❏ Circle or highlight this portion.

> *G2885* κοσμέω *kosmeō* from *G2889*; to *put in proper order,* i.e. *decorate* (literally or figuratively); specifically to *snuff* (a wick):— adorn, garnish, trim.

F. English renderings of the Greek word: Following the meaning, the colon, and the dash mark (:—) are all the different English renderings of the original Greek word. These are the different words that the translators of the King James Version chose to use when translating this particular Greek word into English.

For this Greek word **kosmeo**, the translators chose the words **adorn**, **garnish**, and **trim**. This information is useful if we want to read other verses that include the original Greek word we are studying.

❏ Circle or highlight this portion.

> *G2885* κοσμέω *kosmeō* from *G2889*; to *put in proper order,* i.e. *decorate* (literally or figuratively); specifically to *snuff* (a wick):— adorn, garnish, trim.

G. Based on what you have learned about reading a dictionary entry, answer the following questions about **kosmeo**.

What is the root word of **kosmeo**? _____

What does that root word mean? _____

What does **kosmeo** mean?

_____

What other English words did translators use for **kosmeo**?

_____

Day 6 - More word study

A. Look up the first word (**adorned**) in the concordance (front section) of *Strong's.*

What verse reference is listed first under this word? _____

What number is assigned to it? _____

We will not include this verse in our study of **kosmeo** because it is from the Old Testament. The word translated **adorned** in this verse is not the same original Greek word that we are studying. It is a Hebrew word.

Look up related words online:

1. Go to www.blueletterbible.com

2. In the search box, type other forms of the word you are studying

   • Different tenses of verbs (i.e. adorned)

   • Noun forms (i.e. adornment)

   • Plural form of nouns

B. Look at the next verse listed under **adorned**.

What is its reference? _____

What number is assigned to this verse? _____

This verse uses the exact same Greek word as the one used in 1 Timothy 2:9 that we are studying. Reading this verse will help us better understand what the word means in 1 Timothy.

Read and summarize this verse. (Don't forget to read its context to help you understand its meaning.)

_____

_____

_____

C. The next two verses listed under **adorned** both have the same Strong's number, so they are both useful to our study. Look up both verses and summarize them below. (One of these verses should be familiar from a previous study we have already completed.)

_____

_____

_____

_____

_____

_____

D. Look at the concordance listing again. What word follows **adorned**?

What number is assigned to the verse under this word?

_____

Because this word is not No. 2885 that we are studying, we will not use this verse in our study.

What word follows this one in the concordance?

_____

What number is assigned to the one verse listed under this word?

_____

This is not the exact same number we have been studying, but because it is very close to the same, it is probably a different form of the same word we are studying.

Look up No. 2889 in the Greek dictionary. What do you learn about this word?

_____

_____

_____

Look back at No. 2885. What was the root word for **kosmeo**?

_____

This word, No. 2889, is the root word of the word we are studying in 1 Timothy 2:9. It is actually the noun form of the word. We are studying the verb form.

Look up the verse that contains this word and summarize it. (Is this verse familiar?)

_____

_____

E. Review your notes and summarize all that you have learned about the word **adorn**.

_____

_____

_____

_____

_____

_____

F. Continue your study of **kosmeo** (Strong's G2885, see Days 4-6), by looking up its other English renderings (**garnish** and **trim**) and reading any verses that are assigned the same Strong's number.

Day 7 - Other words

Studying other key words in 1 Timothy 2:9-10 will help us understand what these verses are saying. In this lesson, we will look in detail at **modest**. You probably already have some understanding of these older English words from reading different versions of the Bible. Looking at the original Greek words and at other verses that use these words will further aid us in our study. (Review the instructions from Day 4's lesson to help you with this procedure.)

Interlinear Bible online:

An interlinear Bible displays the verse you are studying along with the text in the original Greek or Hebrew. You can look up 1 Timothy 2:9 in an interlinear Bible online and quickly find all the original words and their definitions.

1. Go to www.biblestudytools.com.

2. Under the "Bible Study" tab, click "Interlinear Bible".

3. Type "1 Timothy 2:9" in the search box and click "search".

4. You will see the verse in English on top, and the verse in the original Greek below. Many of the words in this text are links.

5. Click any of the linked words to view the original word, the definition, and a list of other places that word is used in the bible.

A. Look up the word **modest** in *Strong's*.

What single verse is listed? _____

What number is assigned to the word? _____ Look up this number in the Greek dictionary.

What is the English equivalent of this Greek word (the English word that follows the word written in Greek letters)? _____

Look at the etymology of the word.

What is its root word? _____

What word did we study on Day 5 that is also related to this word?

_____

What is the meaning of this word?

_____

In what other way is it translated?

_____

B. Next we should look up this translation in *Strong's*. However, you won't be able to look up this entire phrase. Look up **behavior**. (If you look up **good**, there will be many more verses to sift through, since it is a more common word.)

Under **behavior,** look for any verses that have the Strong's number 2887. There is only one verse listed. What is it? _____

Read this verse along with its context. Then summarize what you learn about **kosmios** (Strong's No. 2887) from this verse.

_____

_____

_____

C. *Vine's Expository Dictionary of New Testament Words* is another helpful reference tool when studying words in the Bible. It lists English words and then gives information about their corresponding Greek words.

If we look up **modest** in Vine's we will see this:

MODEST

KOSMIOS (κόσμιος), orderly, well-arranged, decent, modest (akin to *kosmos*, in its primary sense as harmonious arrangement, adornment; cp. *kosmikos*, of the world, which is related to *kosmos* in its secondary sense as the world), is used in 1 Tim. 2 : 9 of the apparel with which Christian women are to adorn themselves; in 3 : 2 (R.V., " orderly ;" A.V., " of good behaviour "), of one of the qualifications essential for a bishop or overseer. " The well-ordering is not of dress and demeanour only, but of the inner life, uttering indeed and expressing itself in the outward conversation " (Trench, Syn., §xcii).¶ In the Sept., Eccl. 12 : 9.¶

This information helps give a fuller picture of the word **modest**.

Notice especially the quote from Trench. This helps us remember that modesty and orderliness are not just a matter of dress and outward behavior. They start with a proper orderliness of the soul.

Review and summarize what you have learned from your study of the word **modest**. What do you think modest apparel would look like? Is 1 Timothy 2:9 prescribing a particular style of dress? What is it saying about the heart attitude that should be behind the clothes we wear? How should we relate this information to the fact that Paul is instructing Timothy about public prayer and worship in chapter 2?

_____

_____

_____

_____

_____

_____

_____

Day 8 - More word study

Because women are instructed to adorn themselves "in modest apparel, with shamefacedness and sobriety," we need to understand what these words mean in order to obey them. In this lesson we will study the word **shamefacedness**.

A. Look up **shamefacedness** in Strong's.

What single verse is listed? _____

What number is assigned to the word? _____

Look up this number in the Greek dictionary.

What is the English equivalent of this Greek word (the English word that follows the word written in Greek letters)?

_____

Look at the etymology of the word.

> *G127* αἰδώς *aidōs* perhaps from *G1* (as a negative particle) and *G1492* (through the idea of *downcast eyes*); *bashfulness,* i.e. (towards men), *modesty* or (towards God) *awe:*— reverence, shamefacedness.

A glance at the words referred to (Nos. 1 and 1492) will reveal that this information is more technical than what we need for our study purposes.

Using an online version of Vine's Expository Dictionary of New Testament Words:

• Go to www.blueletterbible.com

• Type "1 Tim 2:9" into search box and click "search."

• To the left of verse 9, click the blue button with the "C" on it. You will see the entire verse in Greek, followed by a chart that lists each English word, its Strong's number, and its original Greek word in root form.

• Scroll down to "adorn" and click its Strong's number.

• Find the "Vine's" box and click on "View Entry".

The main point that is useful to us is the information in parentheses, "through the idea of downcast eyes." This does shed a bit of light on the meaning of **shamefacedness**.

What meanings are given for the word? (Notice that some meanings are in relationship to men and others are in relationship to God.)

_____

_____

_____

B. What other English word is used to translate **aidos**? _____

Look up this word in the concordance. Only one verse under this word is followed by the number 127. It is the only verse that uses the word **aidos** in it.

What is the reference for this verse? _____

Read the verse (and its context) and summarize what you learn about **aidos**.

_____

_____

_____

If we look up **shamefacedness** in *Vine's* we actually find the word **shamefastness** with "A.V. shamefacedness" in parentheses after it. The "A.V." refers to the Authorized Version or what we generally call the King James Version of the Bible.

The Greek word given for **shamefastness/shamefacedness** is the word we have been studying – **aidos**. Vine's describes it as "a sense of shame, modesty . . . used regarding the demeanour of women in the church".

Vine's also quotes from *Bible English*, by Davies:

> *"Shamefastness is that modesty which is 'fast' or rooted in the character . . . The change to 'shamefacedness' is the more to be regretted because shamefacedness . . . has come rather to describe an awkward diffidence, such as we sometimes call sheepishness."*

Based on what you learned from *Strong's* and *Vine's*, is **shamefacedness** a timid, retiring sort of bashfulness? _____

If not, what is it? What would it look like in the church?

_____

_____

_____

Day 9 - More word study

Sobriety in our present-day English is generally associated with temperance or abstinence. A person who is not intoxicated is **sober**. Beyond this, we may also think of a sober person as someone who is solemn and serious and not much fun to be with, the sort of attitude that doesn't sound like a a beautiful, godly way of adorning ourselves.

Sobriety, as it is used in the King James Bible, means more than this. One more word study will help us understand this better.

A. Look up the word **sobriety** in *Strong's*.

What two verses are listed under this word?

_____

_____

What Strong's number is assigned to 1 Timothy 2:9? _____

What number is assigned to the second verse? _____ This tells us that both verses are using the same Greek word.

Read this verse and summarize how the word **sobriety** is used in it.

_____

_____

_____

B. Look up the Strong's number in the Greek dictionary.

> *G4997* σωφροσύνη *sōphrosynē* from *G4998*; *soundness of mind*, i.e. (literally) *sanity* or (figuratively) *self-control:*— soberness, sobriety.

What is the English equivalent of this Greek word? _____

What is the Strong's number for its root word? _____

What is the meaning of **sobriety**?

_____

_____

How is this different from the solemn, boring image we often have of a sober person?

_____

_____

_____

C. Using the Strong's number, look up the meaning of **sophrosyne's** root word. What does this word mean?

_____

_____

_____

D. What other English word is used to translate **sophrosyne**?

_____

Look this word up in the concordance.

Look up the verse that is listed. Read it in several translations. Then summarize what you learn about **soberness** from it. (Don't forget context.)

_____

_____

_____

_____

E. Summarize what you have learned about **sobriety** in this lesson. Is it sad-faced solemnity? Is it something that could make a woman more beautiful? How could this attitude among women enhance public prayer and worship?

_____

_____

_____

_____

_____

_____

_____

_____

Day 10 - Conclusion and application

A. Review what you have learned so far from 1 Timothy 2:9-10.

What does **adorn** mean?

_____

_____

_____

_____

What should women _not_ focus on when adorning themselves?

_____

_____

_____

How _should_ they adorn themselves?

_____

_____

_____

_____

What does **modest** apparel mean?

_____

_____

_____

What does **shamefacedness** mean?

_____

_____

_____

What does **sobriety** mean?

_____

_____

_____

B. Read 1 Timothy 2:10.

According to this verse, with what should women who profess godliness adorn themselves? (We will study this idea in more detail in Study 6.)

_____

C. ✻ Explain what you think this description of a godly woman would look like in the church's prayers and public worship. What roles would the woman fill? What would be her mindset in prayer and worship? What is most important – her appearance or her heart?

_____

_____

_____

_____

_____

D. ✻ Think of at least one woman you know who fits this description of a godly woman in the church.

Describe her.

_____

_____

_____

_____

_____

_____

What can you do to get to know her better? Can you serve alongside her? Can you help in her home? Can you ask her to mentor you? Pray about this and then take action.

_____

_____

_____

_____

_____

E. ✳ Do you think you fit this description of a godly woman and the ways in which she adorns herself? In what areas do you need to submit to God's changing work in your life?

_____

_____

_____

_____

_____

_____

F. Memorize 1 Timothy 2:9-10. Meditate on this verse as you go through your day.

For additional study:

- Following the method used in this study, study Proverbs 31:30-31. Study the main words with the aid of *Strong's Concordance* and its Hebrew dictionary.

- Use *Nave's Topical Bible* to study **humility**. What is humility? How does it relate to feminine modesty?

- Do character studies of different women in the Bible. In what ways did their lives demonstrate sobriety, shamefacedness, and good works? What can you learn from their examples?

- If you have access to the *Treasury of Scripture Knowledge*, read all the verses it lists for 1 Timothy 2:9-10 and summarize what you learn. (You can access *Treasury of Scripture Knowledge* on Biblestudytools.com by clicking the "Library" tab, then "Concordances", then *Treasury of Scripture Knowledge*. You can also use it on Blueletterbible.com by searching for a verse, then clicking on the blue "K" button to the left of the verse's text.)

Study 6

Beauty in Serving

A Word and Topical Study on Good Works

"For we are his workmanship, created in Christ Jesus for good works, which God prepared beforehand, that we should walk in them." (Ephesians 2:10, ESV)

We've seen, in both 1 Peter 3:3-4 and 1 Timothy 2:9-10, that our natural womanly desire to be beautiful should not *focus* on the externals. Real, unfading beauty starts in the heart. It springs from our trust in God's loving and sovereign control of all that comes into our lives. It is displayed in a courageous, peaceful self-control that is willing to follow wherever God leads.

I Timothy 2:10 also says we are adorned through **good works**. What are good works? In this study, we will explore that question. We will study the topic of good works, and we will also learn how to compare two different Greek words that are both translated with the same English word. We will be fairly detailed in our study. Follow the instructions carefully, and when you have finished you will have a better understanding of the good works that adorn a godly woman!

Day 1 - Definitions

Let's start our study by looking up the meanings of both **good** and **works**.

A. Look up the word **good** in *Strong's Exhaustive Concordance*. You will find a very long list of verses that include this word. Skim through the list of references until you find 1 Timothy 2:10.

What Strong's number is assigned to **good** in this verse? _____

B. Look up the information about this word in the Greek dictionary at the back of *Strong's*.

What is the English equivalent or transliteration of this Greek word?

_____

What is the etymology of this word? _____

Notice in this section, the phrase "a prim. word". **Agathos** is a **primary** word. It cannot be further analyzed or broken down, much like a primary color cannot be further broken down. Green, a secondary color, can be broken down into a compound of yellow and blue. However, yellow and

---

Word & Topical Study:

1. Find original words and definitions

2. Read verses using these words

3. Search for your topic in *Nave's Topical Bible* and read passages

4. Summarize and apply

What you will need:

- Bible
- Strong's Concordance
- Nave's Topical Bible

blue are both primary colors. They are starting points, the materials for creating other colors.

Agathos is a starting point. It is a root word, a building block for forming other words.

> *G18* ἀγαθός *agathos* a primary word; *"good"* (in any sense, often as noun):— benefit, good, goods, good things, well. Compare *G2570*.

What is its meaning? _____

Finally, note the different English renderings of this Greek word.

_____

_____

What are the last two words/numbers at the end of this dictionary listing?

_____

These words tell us that we can compare No. 18, **kalos**, with No. 2570, which is another word that is translated as **good** in the English. We will be looking at this word in Day 3's lesson.

C. Now repeat this same process with the word **works**. Look up the word in *Strong's*. This word also appears many times in the Bible, so the list of references in *Strong's* is rather long.

Look for the listing for 1 Timothy 2:10.

What Strong's number is assigned to it? _____

D. Read the information about this word in the Greek dictionary at the back of *Strong's*.

> *G2041* ἔργον *ergon* from a primary (but obsolete)
> ἔργον *ergon* (to *work*); *toil* (as an effort or occupation); by implication an *act:*— deed, doing, labour, work.

What is the English equivalent or transliteration of this Greek word?

_____

What is the etymology of this word?

_____

What is the word's meaning?

_____

Finally, note the different English renderings of this Greek word.

_____

_____

Day 2 - Verses

Now we're ready to read other verses about good works. With *Strong's* we can't look up a listing of verses specifically for **good works**. (If you have a computer, you can do this *much more efficiently* by searching on these two words together. See instructions in the side bar.) If you are using a hard copy of *Strong's Exhaustive Concordance,* you will need to skim through the listing of verses under **good** or **works**, looking for verses that contain the two words together.

A. Compare the list of verses under **good** with the list of verses for **works**. Which list is shorter? _____

Use this list to look for verses about **good works**; you won't have as many references to scan.

B. As you create your list of verses about **good works** to read, look only at New Testament verses in *Strong's,* because we are studying Greek words from the New Testament. These Greek words will not be used in the Old Testament verses.

The list of New Testament verses under **works** is still quite long, and a quick glance shows that most of these verses contain the Greek word **ergon** (Strong's No. 2041) that appears in 1 Timothy 2:10. However, not all these verses contain the words *good* **works**.

In the space below, note references to verses that contain the term **good works**. Note each reference, leaving blank lines below it for recording your notes when you read the verses later.

1. _____

_____

_____

2. _____

_____

_____

3. _____

_____

_____

4. _____

_____

Bible word search online:

1. Go to www.biblestudytools.com or www.biblegateway.com.

2. Find the prominent "search" box, type "good works," and hit enter.

3. You should see a list of all Bible verses that include the phrase "good works".

_____

5. _____

_____

_____

6. _____

_____

_____

7. _____

_____

_____

8. _____

_____

_____

9. _____

_____

_____

10. _____

_____

_____

11. _____

_____

_____

12. _____

_____

_____

13. _____

_____

_____

14. _____

_____

_____

15. _____

_____

_____

16. _____

_____

_____

C. Repeat this same process by looking up **work** (singular) in *Strong's*.
List all the verses under **work** that contain the phrase **good work**. List the
reference now; we will come back to read the verses later.

1. _____

_____

_____

2. _____

_____

_____

3. _____

_____

_____

4. _____

_____

_____

5. _____

_____

_____

6. _____

_____

_____

7. _____

_____

_____

8. _____

_____

_____

9. _____

_____

_____

10. _____

_____

_____

11. _____

_____

_____

D. Before reading all the verses you have listed in Steps B and C, we're going to look at one more detail. The New Testament uses two different Greek words for **good**. One is **agathos** (Strong's No. 18), which is used in 1 Timothy 2:10. The other is **kalos** (No. 2570). These words are very similar in meaning, and both are used when referring to **good works**. We will read the verses that use **agathos** and the verses that use **kalos**. But for our study purposes, we are going to identify which verses use which word.

Turn to the verse listing for the word **good**. Look for each of the references that you listed in Steps B and C above. Note which number is assigned to each verse. For each reference that is followed by the number 18, *circle the reference* in your lists above.

Now we will know which verses use the same word (**agathos**) as the one used in 1 Timothy 2:10.

E. Go back and read all the verses you listed in B and C, summarizing and recording your observations in the lines under each reference. In our next lesson we will look at the difference between **agathos** and **kalos**.

Day 3 - Word differences

In our last lesson, we looked at verses that all contained the English phrases **good works** and **good work**. We are studying these words to better understand the godly woman's adornment – what makes her beautiful.

We saw, by using *Strong's Exhaustive Concordance*, that in the original language of the New Testament two different phrases were used when speaking of good works. Today we will look briefly at the slight differences between those two phrases.

A. In the Greek dictionary at the back of *Strong's* look up No. 2570, **kalos**. You will find this entry:

> *G2570* καλός *kalos* of uncertain affinity; properly *beautiful*, but chiefly (figuratively) *good* (literally or morally), i.e. *valuable* or *virtuous* (for *appearance* or *use*, and thus distinguished from *G18*, which is properly *intrinsic*):— better, fair, good, goodly, honest, meet, well, worthy.

This listing actually makes a brief comparison of **kalos** and **agathos**. As you can see, the words are very similar in meaning. But this definition does make a distinction between the two.

B. Compare this definition with the one for **agathos**.

> *G18* ἀγαθός *agathos* a primary word; *"good"* (in any sense, often as noun):— benefit, good, goods, good things, well. Compare *G2570*.

Without considering the English renderings at the end of each definition, what other differences do you see?

_____

_____

List the English renderings for **kalos**. Remember, the words that follow the dash (–) toward the end of the entry are the English renderings of the Greek word.

_____

_____

_____

_____

List the English listings for **agathos**.

_____

_____

Summarize the differences you see.

_____

_____

C. To further compare **agathos** and **kalos**, let's look at *Vine's Expository Dictionary of New Testament Words*. This resource goes into quite a bit of detail about the word **good**. It addresses different grammatical issues that are beyond the scope of our study. For our purposes, we will only look at portions of its explanation.

Compare the opening sentences for both words:

> GOOD, GOODLY, GOODNESS
> **A. Adjectives.**
> 1. AGATHOS (ἀγαθός) describes that which, being good in its character or constitution, is beneficial in its effect ; it is used (*a*) of things physical, e.g., a tree, Matt. 7 : 17 ; ground, Luke 8 : 8 ; (*b*) in a moral sense,
> under No. 2. See BENEFIT, GOODS.
> 2. KALOS (καλός) denotes that which is intrinsically good, and so, goodly, fair, beautiful, as (*a*) of that which is well adapted to its circumstances or ends, e.g., fruit, Matt. 3 : 10 ; a tree, 12 : 33 ; ground, 13 : 8, 23 ; fish, 13 : 48 ; the Law, Rom. 7 : 16 ; 1 Tim. 1 : 8 ; every creature of

Summarize the differences that you see.

_____

_____

D. More research would help us see that **kalos** is the absolute worth of something. It is ethically good, right, noble, and honorable. It is *visibly* good.

Agathos, in addition to being good, is *beneficial*. It is a goodness that is expressed in acts of kindness that *benefit others*.

One verse in 1 Timothy uses both **agathos** and **kalos** when speaking of good works. Looking at this verse will help us better understand the distinction between the two words. It will also help us understand what Paul means in 1 Timothy 2:10, because both verses are written by him in the same letter to the same person.

E. Read 1 Timothy 5:10. This verse is speaking of the traits of a widow that would be qualified to be supported by the church body.

". . . Well reported of for good (**kalos**) works; if she have brought up children, if she have lodged strangers, if she have washed the saints' feet, if she have relieved the afflicted, if she have diligently followed every good (**agathos**) work."

Can you see how the first reference to good works speaks of her visible reputation and the honorable and noble works that she is known for? The verse then goes on to list several examples of good works that *benefit others*, and ends with the widow following after every good (**agathos**) beneficial work.

List the four specific good works that this widow should be known for:

_____

_____

_____

_____

F. Go back and **reread all of the verses** you listed in Steps B and C of Day 2's lesson. Think about the differences in the two words used for good works. The references you circled use the word **agathos**. The others use **kalos**. Add any additional thoughts to your notes for each verse.

Are both kinds of good works ones that should characterize a godly woman's life? Why?

_____

_____

_____

_____

G. Review your notes from all three days of this study and answer the following questions.

What did God create us to do?

_____

_____

Who enables us to do good works?

_____

_____

Who, in these verses, were doers of good works?

_____

_____

How are we equipped for good works?

_____

_____

Based on what you have learned so far, what sorts of works adorn or beautify a godly woman?

_____

_____

List at least six different examples of good works you can do during this season of your life that will benefit others:

_____

_____

_____

_____

_____

_____

Day 4 - Other verses

Before we use *Nave's Topical Bible* to further study the subject of good works, we are going to look at several other verses that include words and ideas related to the Greek word **agathos**. These will help us better understand the good works that Paul encourages in 1 Timothy 2:10.

A. First we will look at several verses that use the word **agathopoieo**, which means "to be a well-doer". Do you see the root word **agatho** in this word? This word is a verb form of the adjective **agathos**.

Read the following verses and record your observations:

Luke 6:35

_____

_____

_____

1 Peter 2:15

_____

_____

_____

1 Peter 2:20

_____

_____

_____

1 Peter 3:6

_____

_____

_____

1 Peter 3:17

_____

_____

_____

3 John 1:11

_____

_____

_____

B. Based on the preceding verses about **well-doing** or _doing_ good works, answer the following "who-what-where" questions:

Who should we include as beneficiaries of our good works?

_____

_____

_____

_____

_____

What are some examples of well-doing?

_____

_____

_____

What are the results of doing good works?

_____

_____

_____

_____

How do our good works relate to our relationship with God?

_____

_____

_____

What does God think of our well-doing?

_____

_____

_____

How does the doing of good works relate to suffering?

_____

_____

Day 5 - More verses

A. Review what we learned about the beauty of a meek and quiet spirit in 1 Peter 3:3-4 and in our study of 1 Peter 2:11-3:9 (Studies 1 and 2).

How do the verses about **agathopoieo** relate to the beauty of a godly woman's meek and quiet spirit?

_____

_____

Read 1 Peter 3:3-6. How did holy women in "the old time" adorn themselves?

_____

_____

How did Sarah demonstrate her meek and quiet spirit?

_____

_____

How are we Sarah's daughters?

_____

_____

Could this mean that submission to our own husband (or to other authorities over us, whether single or married) is one of the good works of the beautiful and godly woman?

_____

_____

Who benefits from the good work of submission?

_____

_____

_____

B. Let's look at one last word related to **agathos**. The noun form of this Greek word is **agathosune**. It means **goodness**.

Read the following two verses (and their contexts) and record your observations:

Galatians 5:22

_____

_____

_____

Ephesians 5:9

_____

_____

_____

According to these two verses, who is the source of **goodness**?

_____

If this is true, who enables us to perform good works for the benefit of others?

_____

Day 6 - Nave's Topical Bible

We have looked in detail at the Greek words for **good works** and we have looked at their meanings and usage in other passages of Scripture. This approach will help us understand Paul's instruction to women about adorning themselves.

Nave's Topical Bible is the easiest study tool to use when studying a specific topic.

Simply look up the topic and read the verses that are given under that topic.

**Nave's Topical Bible
search online:**

1. Go to
   www.biblestudytools.com.

1. Go to the "Library" tab
   and click "Concordances"
   in the drop-down box.

2. In this list, find "Nave's
   Topical Bible" and click
   on it.

3. Scroll down and you'll see
   links for each letter of the
   alphabet. Click the "W"
   and find "Works".

4. The top of this page lists
   reference links under
   the topic of "WORKS,
   GOOD".

5. If you Ctrl+click these
   links on a PC, they will
   open in a new tab where
   you can read each one.

For more general information about good works, *Nave's Topical Bible* will be helpful. (If you do not own a print copy of *Nave's*, follow the instructions in the sidebar for using an online version.)

A. Look up the word **works**. You will find several categories under this topic. The first one is "Good". Skim through these references and their accompanying notes, looking for any verses that might add to your understanding of **good works**. You will recognize several references as ones we have already read.

Answer the following questions by looking at the verses listed.

What two people are given as examples of those who were doers of good works?

_____

Based on what you know about both of these people, list the good works they did.

_____

_____

_____

_____

_____

_____

_____

_____

Who were their beneficiaries?

_____

_____

_____

How did those beneficiaries respond to their good works?

_____

_____

_____

What are some purposes of good works?

_____

_____

_____

B. Skim the section under **works** entitled "Unclassified Scriptures relating to:" (Some verses will be ones we have already read.) Answer the following questions, based on what you read.

How do our good works relate to our service to Jesus?

_____

_____

_____

_____

_____

_____

What should our attitude and motivation be when doing good works?

_____

_____

_____

_____

_____

What do these verses say about people who profess faith in Jesus but fail to demonstrate that faith through good works?

_____

_____

_____

_____

What is the source of our ability to do good works?

_____

_____

_____

Nave's Topical Bible

This Bible study tool was created over 100 years ago by a US Army chaplain, Orville J. Nave. He studied the King James Bible and labored for 14 years, along with his wife Anna, his "indefatigable assistant," to create the best-known topical Bible we have today. Earlier topical Bibles only covered a few topics and wouldn't include a passage in more than one category, even if it was relevant to multiple topics. Nave's Topical Bible contains more than 100,000 Bible verses organized under 20,000 different topics. This study tool is much more complete, and therefore more useful to everyone.

"Its preparation was inspired by the obvious deficiency of such helps in the use of the Scriptures. This deficiency was felt by the author in preparing sermons, lectures, and other forms of religious instruction. The quiet of army garrisons, apart from the rush and distraction of dense communities, has been favorable to its careful preparation. With the belief that it will contribute to make the Scriptures more quickly, easily, and fully available where particular subjects are under consideration, I offer it to the public." – Orville Nave

What is God's plan for us in doing good works?

_____

_____

_____

How are we prepared and equipped for good works?

_____

_____

_____

What are some examples of good works?

_____

_____

_____

_____

What are the rewards for doing good works?

_____

_____

_____

_____

Day 7 - Summarize and apply

Today we will review what we have learned and then prayerfully consider how to put that learning into *action*.

A. Review your notes from this entire lesson. Then write a **short essay**, summarizing what you have learned about **good works**. What is their place in a believer's life and, more specifically, in a believing woman's life? How are we equipped for them? What do they look like? With what attitude should they be done? Who are they for?

_____

_____

_____

_____

_____

_____

_____

_____

_____

_____

_____

_____

_____

_____

_____

_____

_____

_____

_____

B. Read James 2:14-26. The Greek word for **works** in this passage is **ergon**. This is the same word that appears in the phrase **good works**. Although these verses do not specifically address **good works**, they do speak about the importance of actually _doing_, and _doing_ is essential to **good works**.

According to James, what is the relationship between our professed faith and our works?

_____

_____

_____

To what does James liken a faith that is not accompanied by works?

_____

What else does this passage say about works?

_____

_____

_____

C. A real saving faith in Jesus will be demonstrated in our actions. What we do is *evidence* of our faith, but we must always remember that our works don't *replace* our faith. We are saved by *faith alone*. But true faith is not just words or feelings; it is accompanied by action. Faith is the root; our works are the fruit that grows from that root. If there is no fruit, the root is dead.

In thinking about the good works that adorn a godly woman's life, we should always remember that this adornment *starts in the heart*. Good works – works that serve and bless and benefit others – start with *faith*. They spring from our love for Jesus, who suffered and died for us. Without the love that only Jesus can plant in our hearts, the love that grows out of our appreciation for *His* great love, all our "good" works will amount to nothing.

Answer the following questions.

Do you profess faith in Jesus and His saving work on the cross? _____

If so, is your faith demonstrated by your works? _____

Would others say that your life is characterized by **good works** that are done for the blessing and benefit of others? _____

As you go through the day, do you look for ways to work for the benefit of others?

_____

✳ Do you invest more time and energy each day in serving others than you do in caring for your physical appearance?

_____

Are there good works in your household that you could be doing for the benefit of others? If so, list them.

_____

_____

_____

_____

_____

_____

_____

_____

D. Pray for the Holy Spirit's guidance. In what ways does God want you to change the way you think about yourself and about others?

_____

_____

_____

_____

_____

_____

_____

E. What changes is God calling you to make in your actions? What will you do differently? Write down at least one specific goal that will help you apply what you have learned in this lesson.

_____

_____

_____

_____

_____

_____

For additional study:

• Using the method outlined in Study 3, study the account of Dorcas in Acts 9:36-43.

• Read the Gospels, noting each good work that is recorded in the accounts of Jesus's life. What can you learn from His example of good works?

• Under the listing for "Works, Good" in *Nave's Topical Bible*, find the references for parables relating to good works. Study these parables and read commentaries that explain their meaning.

• Use a concordance, *Nave's Topical Bible*, and commentaries to study the relationship of our works to our faith.

• Use the method outlined in Study 8 to study 1 Corinthians 13. How does this chapter relate to the godly woman's practice of good works?.

Beauty without Discretion

A Verse Study of Proverbs 11:22

"As a jewel of gold in a swine's snout, so is a fair woman which is without discretion." (Proverbs 11:22)

As we've seen in 1 Timothy 2:9-10, beauty is more than *just* external. There's nothing wrong with outer beauty. But outwardly beautiful women can be ugly inside, and a beautiful woman without discretion and wisdom can be pretty disgusting. In this study, we'll see what the Bible says about that kind of woman.

Day 1 - Read and look for marginal notes

A. Read Proverbs 11:22 in at least three different translations. Reading in different translations will help you understand a verse better.

After reading, copy the verse from the King James Version.

_____

_____

_____

_____

B. To start digging deeper into the meaning of this proverb, we are going to first use the **marginal notes** that are included in most Bibles. These notes often point us to other verses that will deepen our understanding of the verse we are studying.

Many styles of marginal notes exist. You may need to refer to the beginning pages of your Bible for an explanation of its particular cross-referencing system.

Look carefully at Proverbs 11:22 in your Bible. Besides the obvious text of the verses and the verse numbers, do you see any other small numbers or letters in the verses? Some Bibles also have a column of small words in one of the margins or between the columns of Scripture text.

If you don't see these numbers, letters, or small words, examine other Bibles in your home until you find one with marginal references. Most study Bibles should have the marginal references we need for this study. Looking at an actual Bible where you can see the notes will help you better understand the explanation offered here.

Verse study:

1. Read and copy the verse

2. Study marginal notes

3. Study key words

4. Make comparisons and draw conclusions

5. Apply

What you will need:

• Bible

• Several Bibles with marginal notes

• Strong's Concordance

• English dictionary

Common types of marginal notes:

- **Textual notes** give information related to the translation and original languages. These notes may tell you about other possible translations of a word or about small differences in the text of the original manuscripts.

- **Cross-references** point you to other Bible verses that are related to the ones you are reading.

- **Other notes** often explain unfamiliar terms and units of measure.

Most Bibles with marginal references mark words and phrases within the verse with **superscript** numbers and letters. This means that the letters and numbers are **smaller** and **raised higher** than the rest of the type in the text.

In the page's reference column (found in the margin or in the center column), bold numbers will indicate verse numbers, and after each verse number will appear any notes pertaining to that particular verse.

C. Below is an example of one type of a marginal note. This is a **textual note**. These notes often shed light on a word's meaning or list other possible readings of the verse. They may also indicate sections that vary from one manuscript to another. Textual notes are most often noted with superscript numbers.

> **20** *Lit way*
> *Ps 119:1; Prov 13:6*
> *1 Chr 29:17*
>
> **21** *Lit Hand to hand* *Lit seed*
>
> **22** *Lit taste*
> *Gen 24:47*
>
> **23** *Prov 10:28*
>
> But the descendants of the righteous will be delivered.
> 22 As a ring of gold in a swine's snout
> So is a beautiful woman who lacks discretion.
> 23 The desire of the righteous is only good,
> But the expectation of the wicked is wrath.
> 24 There is one who scatters, and yet increases all the more,

Notice the superscript numeral 1 in front of the word **discretion**. If you look under verse 22 in the marginal notes in the left hand margin, you will see "*1* Lit *taste*". **Circle this in the example.** This note tells us that the word translated as **discretion** in this *New Inductive Study Bible* (NASB) literally means *taste*.

You can also see a small superscript "a" in front of the word **ring**. Look at the marginal notes for verse 22 in the left hand margin. What is listed after "a"?

_____

Using BlueletterBible online to find cross-references:

1. Go to www.blueletterbible.com

2. Type "Prov. 11:22" into the search box and click search.

3. Scroll down to verse 22 and click on the blue box with the "K", to the left of the verse. This takes you to The Treasury of Scripture Knowledge, which is a comprehensive listing of cross-references for every verse in the Bible.

4. Read the verses that are listed under different key words from Prov. 11:22.

This type of marginal note is called a **cross-reference**. Cross-references lead you to other verses that address a similar topic or contain the same word or a similar word.

Look up this verse. How does this relate to Proverbs 11:22?

_____

_____

D. The next example is from a standard King James Version Bible. This Bible includes three marginal notes for the verse. One is a textual note. It is keyed with a superscript numeral 3. The other two are cross-references, and they are indicated with superscript letters.

> 22 As a ^{3e} jewel of gold in a ^{f} swine's snout, so is a fair woman which is without discretion.
> 23 The desire of the righteous is only good; but the ^{h} expectation of
>
> Ps. 112. 2
> d ch. 10. 25
> 3 Or *ring*
> e ch. 25. 12
> Jb. 42. 11
> f Ps. 80. 13
> Mt. 7. 6
> g ch. 11. 20

As you can see, the word **jewel** has two notes. One is a textual note; the other is a cross-reference that includes two verse references. Both the superscript number (for textual note) and letters (for cross-references) are listed before the word **jewel**.

What other translation does the textual note offer for the word **jewel**?

_____

_____

What two references does the cross reference list?

_____

_____

Read these two verses and note how they relate to Proverbs 11:22.

_____

_____

_____

Going on in the verse, we see a superscript "f" before the word **swine's**. Note these two references, then read and summarize the verses.

_____

_____

_____

Day 2 - More cross-references

A. Other Bibles list the following **cross-references** for Proverbs 11:22. Read and summarize these verses.

Ring – Numbers 31:51

_____

_____

_____

Gold – 1 Kings 10:21

_____

_____

_____

Swine's – Deuteronomy 14:8

_____

_____

Using marginal references at Biblegateway.com:

1. Go to www.biblegateway.com and look up Proverbs 11:22 in the verse search box.

2. This should bring up the text of the verse. Above this text, you should see a button for "page options".

3. Click the "page options" button, and you should see a list of check boxes for "footnotes," "cross-references," etc. Check these buttons to show the marginal notes. Links for each cross-reference will be displayed below the verse text.

Using marginal references at Biblestudytools.com:

Go to www.biblestudytools.com and look up Proverbs 11:22

1. You will see check boxes for "cross-references" and "footnotes". Check both of these boxes, and super-script letters will appear within the text of the verse. You can hover over these letters, and the cross-references will pop up.

2. You can also click the "cross-references" link **below** the verse to display all the cross-references below the verse text. You can Ctrl+click these links to open a new window with the full text of each cross-reference.

Interpreting Scripture with Scripture

"The infallible rule of interpretation of scripture is the scripture itself; and therefore, when there is a question about the true and full sense of any scripture, it must be searched and known by other places that speak more clearly."

The Westminster Confession of Faith, 1646

A note about notes:

It is important to remember that marginal notes are not the divinely inspired Word of God. They are editors' notes, written by scholars who have studied the Bible and its original languages. These notes are not infallible. They are influenced by the editors' theology and by different understandings of languages and words.

Another **textual note** tells us that the phrase "is without discretion" can also be translated as "turneth aside from" discretion.

B. Look for marginal notes in any other Bibles you have in your home. Note any new references, read the verses, and record what you learn.

Ref.:   Notes:

_____

_____

_____

_____

_____

_____

_____

_____

C. Summarize anything new you have learned from your study of cross-references for Proverbs 11:22.

_____

_____

_____

_____

_____

_____

_____

_____

_____

_____

_____

_____

Day 3 - Word study

When studying a short verse or proverb like this, careful study of the main words will also help us understand its meaning better.

Use *Strong's Exhaustive Concordance* to identify the Hebrew words for each of these main words from Proverbs 11:22. Note each word's Strong's number, its meaning, and the other ways it is translated. (See Study 5 for a review of this procedure.)

Word Study Chart

KJV Word	Strong's #	Hebrew word	Meaning of word	Other translations
Jewel				
Gold				
Swine's				
Fair				
Discretion				

Searching on a
Strong's number with
Blueletterbible.com:

Using an online Bible study
site will make word studies
much easier!

1. Go to www.blueletterbible.
com

2. Type "jewel" in the search
box, and select KJV in the
"version" box.

3. Click search. This will take
you to a concordance listing for every appearance of
the English word "jewel"
in the King James Version.

4. Scroll down to Proverbs
11:22. The word "jewel"
will appear in red.

5. Note the blue number that
follows the word "jewel".
This is the Strong's num-
ber assigned to the original
Hebrew word in Proverbs
11:22.

6. Click that blue Strong's
number. This will open
a lexicon listing for the
Hebrew word. The listing
tells you all about this
Hebrew word – how to say
it, what it means, what part
of speech it is, the other
ways it is translated into
English, and how many
times the word appears in
the Bible.

7. In addition to all this
information, you can also
read *every verse in the
Bible that contains this
same Hebrew word!* Under
"Concordance Results
Using KJV", the text
for every verse is given,
with the significant word
marked with the Strong's
number in red.

Day 4 - Word study continued

Note: If you have access to the Internet, the word studies in Days 4-6 will
be much easier if you follow the steps outlined in the sidebar, using Blue
Letter Bible online.

A. Look back at the chart on the previous page. What other English word
is used for **jewel**? _____

Look this word up in *Strong's Concordance*. Notice all the verses that
share the same Strong's number, H5141. These all contain the same
original Hebrew word that is translated as **jewel** in Proverbs 11:22.

EARRING
Gen 24:22 took a golden **e** of half a shekel weight,   H5141
         30 And it came to pass, when he saw the **e**   H5141
         47 him: and I put the **e** upon her face, and   H5141
Job 42:11 of money, and every one an **e** of gold.   H5141
Prv 25:12 *As* an **e** of gold, and an ornament of   H5141

Skim these verse excerpts to get an idea of how the word is used in other
Scripture passages. Turn to the Bible and read entire verses, if desired, to
get a better picture.

Based on your observations, what were the main purposes or uses of the
gold earring or **jewel of gold** in the Old Testament?

_____

_____

_____

B. Look up in *Strong's* the other English words that you listed for gold on
your chart (p. 85). There will be a long list of verses. Look for any verses
that share the same Strong's number. Simply skim these to get an idea of
how gold was generally used in Scripture.

List some of the primary uses of gold as described in the Bible.

_____

_____

_____

Day 5 - Word study continued

A. Repeat the procedure used on Day 4 for the other translations of **swine**.
(You may need to read entire verses, rather than concordance excerpts, to
get a complete picture of this word.)

What was the attitude toward **swine** in Jewish culture? (Read New Testament verses as well as Old Testament to get a better understanding of
this.)

_____

_____

_____

B. Repeat the same procedure for other translations of the word **fair**.

List the names of all the people who are described in Scripture as **beautiful**, **fair**, and **goodly**.

_____

_____

_____

Do these people share any common traits or circumstances? If so, what?

_____

_____

_____

Why do you think this might be?

_____

_____

_____

Day 6 - Word study continued

A. Continue with the same procedure described in Day 4 for other translations of **discretion**.

In what different ways is the word for **discretion** used? Do you see any common factors in its various uses?

_____

_____

_____

B. Review all your notes from Days 3-6 and think about how they all relate to each other and to Proverbs 11:22. What have you learned that helps you better understand Proverbs 11:22?

_____

_____

_____

Strong's number search in e-Sword

The **KJV + Strong's Numbers Bible** in e-Sword (a free Windows program) is a powerful tool for studying original words in the Bible. It will help you find the definitions and usage of a word much faster.

1. Install **e-Sword** from www.e-sword.net (or buy the e-Sword iPad app).

2. The basic program comes with two Bibles, the KJV, plus the KJV with Strong's Numbers. Click on the "KJV+" tab to use the version with Strong's numbers.

3. You will see the Bible text with green superscript numbers beside most of the words in each verse. These numbers correspond to each Hebrew or Greek word in the original text. If you hover over these numbers, you will see the original word and its definition.

4. You can search the text of the KJV+ Bible by hitting "Ctrl+S" or clicking the little binoculars icon. You can search for English words, or you can search for Hebrew or Greek words by searching for the Strong's number.

5. The resulting list gives you **all the verses** that use that Hebrew or Greek word. By looking for the highlighted number in each verse, you can see where the word was used, and what English word was used to translate it..

Day 7 - Additional word study

Answer the following questions to help you continue to meditate on the meaning of Proverbs 11:22.

A. Copy a dictionary's definition of **discretion**.

_____

_____

_____

B. Copy a dictionary's definition of **advice**.

_____

_____

_____

C. Copy a dictionary's definition of **taste**.

_____

_____

_____

D. What additional insights do you gain from these definitions that add to your understanding of Proverbs 11:22?

_____

_____

_____

E. From what you have learned so far, how would you describe a woman "without discretion"?

_____

_____

_____

F. Use a dictionary or other reference book to research the use of nose rings on pigs. What is their purpose? Of what are they usually made?

_____

_____

_____

G. Would there be any benefit in making a pig's nose ring out of gold?

_____

H. Review your notes about **gold** and **swine** from Day 3's study. Based on what you have learned about the uses of gold and the dietary laws and attitudes about pigs in Jewish culture, how appropriate would a gold ring be in a pig's snout?

_____

_____

I. Do you believe that beauty is wasted in some way on a woman who does not have discretion, good judgment, and an appetite for godly living? If so, in what ways?

_____

_____

_____

Nose rings

Pigs naturally like to dig and root with their noses, looking for things to eat in the soil. This can damage the area they live in or even their own noses. To discourage this habit, rings are often placed in their noses. These rings are usually made of copper, with sharp ends that are clipped to the nose. When the pig roots in loose leaves and other vegetation, the ring simply moves back and forth. If the pig attempts to dig in hard soil or flooring, the ring will cause enough pain to make him stop.

Day 8 - Comparisons and conclusions

A. Read the following pairs of verses and compare what is said about pigs with what is said about foolish women.

Leviticus 11:7 and Proverbs 5:8

_____

_____

_____

Deuteronomy 14:8 and 1 Kings 11:1-11

_____

_____

_____

Matthew 7:6 and Proverbs 5:3-6

_____

_____

_____

Psalm 80:8-13 and Proverbs 14:1

_____

_____

_____

B. Review what you have learned from all the lessons in this study. Then write a paraphrase of Proverbs 11:22 in your own words:

_____

_____

_____

_____

Day 9 - Review and Application

A. Write a short essay that describes the woman without discretion and then discuss how a *beautiful* woman without discretion is like a gold ring in a pig's snout.

_____

_____

_____

_____

_____

_____

_____

_____

_____

_____

_____

_____

_____

_____

_____

_____

_____

_____

_____

B. ✳ Pray about what you have learned. In what ways is God calling you to think differently?

_____

_____

_____

_____

_____

C. ✳ In what ways is God calling you to behave differently?

_____

_____

_____

_____

_____

_____

D. ✳ Share what you have learned with your parents. Pray for the Holy Spirit's changing work in your heart, and commit to specific actions that will help you grow in wisdom and discretion. List at least one specific action you will take to better apply what you have learned.

_____

_____

_____

_____

_____

For additional study:

- Using the method outlined in Study 6, do a topical study of the fool. What is he? How does he act? What are the results of his foolishness? How, specifically, does the foolish woman behave?

- Read the book of Proverbs and note every verse that likens a woman to something else. To what are women compared? Study these verses, using the method we followed in our study of Proverbs 11:22.

- Use Strong's Concordance to help you study the **strange woman** as she is described in Scripture. What is she like? What are Scripture's warnings regarding her? What is her affect on men?

- Read the book of Proverbs, taking notes on every reference to **wisdom**. What is wisdom? Where does it come from? What are its affects in our lives? How do you think it relates to **discretion**?

Beauty under Pressure

A Chapter Study of 1 Samuel 25

"...and the name of his wife Abigail: and she was a woman of good understanding, and of a beautiful countenance..." (1 Samuel 25:3b)

In the last study, we looked at what the Bible says about a beautiful woman who has no discretion. In this lesson, we'll study the words and actions of a beautiful woman with discretion – and how she quickly mobilized to pacify an angry future king and save the lives of her entire household.

Day 1 - Background and overview

A. Read 1 Samuel 24-26. This will help you understand the events of David's life that precede and follow his encounter with Abigail.

Write a summary sentence for each chapter.

Chapter 24

_____

_____

Chapter 25

_____

_____

Chapter 26

_____

_____

B. Reread Chapter 25.

Who are the main characters in this account?

_____

_____

_____

Chapter study:
1. Background/overview
2. Main characters
3. Key words/themes
4. Cross-references
5. Details
6. Commentaries
7. More related verses
8. Summary/application

What you will need:
• Bible
• Colored pencils
• Study Bible with cross references
• *Matthew Henry's Commentary on the Whole Bible*

Where does the story take place?

_____

Summarize the story.

_____

_____

_____

_____

_____

C. Make a timeline of this story by listing all the main events in chronological order.

Chapter 24 David spares Saul's life

_____

_____

_____

_____

_____

_____

_____

_____

_____

_____

_____

_____

_____

_____

Chapter 26 David spares Saul's life

Day 2 - Main characters

Reread Chapter 25. As you read, highlight with ORANGE every mention of **Nabal**. Mark his name and every pronoun (his, he, I, my, etc.) that refers to him.

Note what is said about Nabal in this chapter.

_____

_____

_____

_____

_____

Day 3 - Main characters

Read Chapter 25 again. Highlight in BLUE every mention of **David** (including pronouns referring to him).

Note what is said about David in this chapter.

_____

_____

_____

_____

_____

_____

Day 4 - Main characters

Read Chapter 25 one more time. Highlight in GREEN every mention of **Abigail** (including pronouns referring to her).

Note what is said about Abigail in this chapter.

_____

_____

_____

_____

_____

_____

_____

_____

Day 5 - Key words and themes

A. Reread Chapter 25.

List at least two repeated words or phrases that you think are significant in this chapter.

_____

_____

B. Select and copy one verse that reflects the main message or theme of the chapter.

_____

_____

_____

_____

_____

_____

C. Before we study Abigail's appeal and David's response, use *Strong's Concordance* to look up the meanings of the following words. Use the method outlined in Study 5 to find and record the Strong's number for each word as it is used in 1 Samuel 25. Then look up the word's explanation in the **Hebrew** dictionary at the back of *Strong's*. Note any helpful information you find for each word and how it relates to our study of 1 Samuel 25.

Churlish (vs. 3) No. _____

_____

_____

_____

Belial (vs. 17, 25) No. _____

_____

_____

_____

Folly (vs. 25) No. _____

_____

_____

_____

How does the study of **churlish**, **Belial**, and **folly** help you better understand Nabal and his character?

_____

_____

_____

_____

Day 6 - More key words and themes

A. Continue studying key words from 1 Samuel 25, following the same instructions from part C of Day 5.

Shed blood (vs. 26, 31, 33) No. _____

_____

_____

_____

Avenge (vs. 26, 31, 33) No. _____

_____

_____

_____

How does the study of the words **shed blood** and **avenge** help you better understand David and his character?

_____

_____

_____

_____

Interlinear Bible online

An interlinear Bible displays the verse you are studying along with the text in the original Greek or Hebrew. You can look up verses from 1 Samuel 25 in an interlinear Bible online and quickly find all the original words and their definitions.

1. Go to www.biblestudytools.com.

2. Under the "Bible Study" tab, click "Interlinear Bible".

3. Type "1 Samuel 25:3" in the search box and click "search".

4. You will see the verse in English on top, and the verse in the original Greek below. Many of the words in this text are links.

5. Click any of the linked words to view the original word, the definition, and a list of other places that word is used in the Bible.

Understanding (vs. 3) No. _____

_____

_____

_____

Beautiful (vs. 3) No. _____

_____

_____

_____

Lord (vs. 24-41) No. _____

_____

_____

_____

Advice (vs. 33) No. _____

_____

_____

_____

How does your study of **understanding**, **beautiful**, **lord**, and **advice** give you a better understanding of Abigail and her character?

_____

_____

_____

_____

B. Look back at the words we studied in Study 7. What two words in this lesson did we also study in Proverbs 11:22?

_____

Does the study of these words help you better understand the meaning of Proverbs 11:22? If so, how?

_____

_____

_____

Day 7 - Cross-references

A. If your Bible doesn't have cross-references, find a study Bible that does. Find and list all cross-references for 1 Samuel 25. Note the verse from 1 Samuel 25 along with its cross-reference. Then look up each verse and summarize what it says or how it relates to the chapter we are studying.

Verse: Cross-ref.:   Verse summary:

_____

_____

_____

_____

_____

_____

_____

_____

_____

_____

_____

B. Summarize what you have learned from your study of the chapter's cross-references.

_____

_____

_____

_____

_____

_____

Using BlueLetterBible to search for cross-references online:

If you have Internet access, use *The Treasury of Scripture Knowledge* at www.blueletterbible.com to do this study.

1. Go to www.blueletterbible.com.

2. Search on "1 Sam. 25".

3. For each verse in 1 Samuel 25, click on the blue "K" button to the left of the text. This brings up verse listings from *The Treasury of Scripture Knowledge*. These are cross-references to all the key words in the verse.

4. You can click on the "K" button for each verse to see any cross references that relate to that verse.

5. You will need to be selective. Choose words that you are particularly interested in. Skim the verses related to these words, noting any significant information and observations.

The Treasury of Scripture Knowledge was first published around 1830. It is a collection of over 500,000 cross-references, showing only chapter and verse citations with no text. It is organized like a Bible, beginning with Genesis and ending with Revelation. Each verse is cross-referenced to several others to help the reader gain a true sense of how a word or phrase is used in the Bible. This also helps the reader interpret Scripture with Scripture. The book is usually attributed to R. A. Torrey, but he did not actually write it. He only promoted it.

Day 8 - Details

Reread 1 Samuel 25, looking for answers to the following questions.

A. List all the words that indicate David's humility in asking Nabal for food.

_____

_____

_____

_____

B. What reasons did David have for believing Nabal would provide food for him and his men?

_____

_____

_____

_____

C. How do David's words in this account differ from his attitude and words in 1 Samuel 25:13, 21-22, and 34?

_____

_____

_____

_____

D. How many times does Nabal use the words **I** and **my** in his response to David's men? _____

What does this tell us about Nabal?

_____

E. What does Nabal insinuate about David when he responds to his men?

_____

_____

_____

_____

F. Read 1 Samuel 17 and 1 Samuel 18:5-7.

Do you think Nabal really didn't know who David was? _____

If he *did* know who David was, why do you think he responded the way he did?

_____

_____

Day 9 - More details

Continue reading 1 Samuel 25 and answer the questions below.

A. Abigail's speed of action is mentioned four times in 1 Samuel 25. Look for these words and circle them in your Bible. Why do you think the writer of 1 Samuel chose to include this detail in his account?

_____

_____

_____

B. List all the words and actions that demonstrate Abigail's humility when appealing to David.

_____

_____

_____

_____

C. Circle each time Abigail refers to David as "my lord". How many times does this happen? _____

D. How does David respond to Abigail's appeal?

Blessed be _____

Blessed be _____

Blessed be _____

E. Who does David credit for restraining him from hurting Abigail and her household?

_____

F. Read 1 Samuel 25:19. Why do you think the author inserted this detail into the middle of his account?

_____

_____

G. What was Nabal doing while Abigail was pleading for the lives of their entire household?

_____

_____

H. Why do you think Abigail waited until after the crisis to talk to Nabal?

_____

_____

I. Summarize any new insights you have gained from your study in Days 8 and 9.

_____

_____

_____

_____

_____

_____

_____

_____

Day 10 - Commentaries

A good Bible commentary can often help you answer questions you have as you are studying your Bible. For this study, we will use *Matthew Henry's Commentary on the Whole Bible* to help us address some questions about David's and Abigail's actions, as well as any other questions you may have. (See sidebar for reading *Matthew Henry* online, if needed.)

A. Read 1 Samuel 25, noting any questions you have or any issues that are unclear to you.

_____

_____

_____

_____

_____

B. Look up 1 Samuel 25 in *Matthew Henry* and use it to answer the following questions.

Online commentaries:

- Matthew Henry's commentary, and several others, are online at www.biblestudytools.com. Go to their site and click on the "commentaries" tab. You can also get the entire set of Matthew Henry's commentaries at a small cost in the Amazon Kindle store.

- Free Bible commentaries can also be downloaded with e-Sword and some mobile apps (see page 6).

Why did David respond so rashly to Nabal after showing so much restraint when he had opportunities to kill Saul?

_____

_____

_____

_____

Why was it not wrong for Abigail to speak of her husband as she did when appealing to David?

_____

_____

_____

Why did Abigail not tell Nabal what she was doing?

_____

_____

_____

Why was it not wrong for her to be giving food to David and his men after her husband had refused them?

_____

_____

_____

Look for answers to any other questions that you have about this account.

_____

_____

_____

_____

_____

_____

_____

Matthew Henry's Commentary:

Matthew Henry was a Presbyterian minister who lived from 1662 to 1714. His father Phillip gathered his family every day for morning and evening devotions, where he would read a Scripture passage, explain it, and encourage the children to write their own notes. Although he was often in poor health, Matthew had an aptitude for study, and it is said that he could read the Bible by age three. (He also learned Latin, Greek, and Hebrew.)

At age twenty-three, he went to London to study law, but he found it unsatisfying and returned home after only one year. It was then that a friend asked him to preach, and he discovered the work God had designed him for. So great was his enthusiasm for the gospel, and so thorough was his preparation for each sermon, that other churches soon began asking him to come and preach.

Before long, he was offered a pastorate in the town of Chester, and he served there as a pastor for over twenty-five years. Toward the end of his life, he gathered his many notes from Bible study and preaching and wrote a commentary on the entire Old Testament, along with the Gospels and the book of Acts. Sadly, he died before his commentary on the New Testament was finished. Henry's pastor friends realized the value of his practical, easily understandable commentary, and they used his notes on Romans through Revelation to complete the project and produce the Bible commentary that has been widely used ever since.

Day 11 - Related verses

A. Copy Proverbs 11:22.

_____

_____

_____

_____

B. Copy Proverbs 25:12.

_____

_____

_____

_____

C. Circle the words **earring of gold** (or the words that are used in your translation) in both verses above. These words are the same Greek words in both proverbs. They mean the same thing.

D. In 1 Samuel 25, Abigail is described as **beautiful**. In your written copy of Proverbs 11:22, draw a box around the word **fair** (or the word that is used in your translation). This is the same Greek word that is used to describe Abigail.

E. In 1 Samuel 25, when David responds to Abigail's counsel, he commends her for her **discretion**. In your written copy of Proverbs 11:22, underline the word **discretion**. This is the same Greek word that is used to describe Abigail.

F. Write a short essay that explains how Proverbs 25:12 and Proverbs 11:22 relate to the story of Abigail.

_____

_____

_____

_____

_____

_____

_____

_____

_____

_____

_____

_____

_____

_____

_____

_____

_____

_____

_____

_____

_____

_____

_____

_____

_____

_____

_____

Day 12 - Summary and application

A. Review what you have learned in this study and in Studies 1 and 2. Explain how respectful appeal and discretion relate to the godly beauty of a meek and quiet spirit.

_____

_____

_____

For further study:

- Study other appeals in Scripture. How does Esther's appeal to Ahasuerus compare to Abigail's appeal to David? Study Bathsheba's appeal to David in 1 Kings 1:11-31. How are these appeals alike? How are they different? What can you learn from them? What can you apply to your relationships with parents, teachers, and other authorities?

- How should we treat an angry person, or a person who treats us or others unjustly? Study the Bible to answer this question.

- Study David's interactions with Saul in 1 Samuel. How did he respond to Saul's wrongs against him? What reasons does he give for responding in this way? Why do you think he responded differently to Nabal?

- Read 1 Samuel 25:34. What did David say would have happened if Abigail had not hurried to intercept him?

- Use *The Treasury of Scripture Knowledge* to study times when it is appropriate to hurry or "make haste".

  1. Go to www.blueletter-bible.com
  2. Search for "1 Sam. 25:34".
  3. Click the blue "K" button to the left of the verse.
  4. Read all the verses listed under the word "hasted".

- Use *Nave's Topical Bible* to study the topic of **counsel**. What is the role of counsel in our lives? What are the benefits of seeking counsel? What are the results of rejecting wise counsel?

B. Review what you learned in Study 5. Do you believe that Abigail's actions and appeal are good works like those that should adorn a godly woman? Why or why not?

C. ✻ In what specific ways is God calling you to change your actions and thinking?

D. Pray and thank God for His grace and strength that will enable you to make these changes.

Beauty in the Gates

A Book Study of Ruth

"And now, my daughter, fear not; I will do to thee all that thou requirest: for all the city of my people doth know that thou art a virtuous woman." (Ruth 3:11)

The book of Ruth is a beautiful love story and a beautiful picture of God's loving redemption of His people. Ruth is also a wonderful picture of godly character and beauty. She is the **one** woman in the Bible who is identified as a **virtuous** woman.

Boaz says in Ruth 3:11, "…for all the city of my people doth know that thou art a virtuous woman." The word that Boaz used to describe Ruth is the same word that is used in Proverbs 31 to describe the virtuous woman that every man should seek.

This same word is also used to describe brave and strong men of character, "mighty men of valor." Ruth could be called a "mighty woman of valor", and like the Proverbs 31 mighty woman of valor, she was praised in the gates. The people of the city knew that she was a virtuous woman. They knew from her **actions**.

This study will take several days. For our study purposes, we will focus on Ruth and her actions and words, with some time devoted to other characters and themes in the book. Several more days could be spent studying Naomi, Boaz, and the theme of redemption in this book. Additional study ideas (at the end of this study) will help you learn much more from this beautiful story of love and redemption.

Day 1 - Pray and read

Begin your study with prayer. Read the entire book of Ruth, preferably in one sitting.

Day 2 - Read again

Read the entire book of Ruth again, in a different translation this time. Then write a brief summary of the story in the space below.

_____

_____

_____

_____

Book study:

1. Pray and read

2. Read again

3. Background info

4. Summarize

5. Look for important themes, words, and characters

6. Review

7. Application

What you will need:

• Two Bibles in different translations

• Strong's Concordance

• Study Bible, commentary, or Bible dictionary

• Colored pencils

_____

_____

_____

Day 3 - Background information

Get some background information about the book of Ruth. Use a study Bible, commentary, or Bible dictionary to answer the following questions:

A. What literary style is the book? _____

B. Who wrote the book of Ruth? (The answer to this question is uncertain. Describe the different opinions and the reasons for and against each. Which one do you think is correct?)

_____

_____

_____

_____

_____

C. When was the book written? (This is also uncertain. Describe different opinions and the reasons for and against them. Which one do you think is correct?)

_____

_____

_____

_____

D. When does the story take place?

_____

_____

E. Where does the story take place?

_____

_____

F. What historical events preceded the time of this story?

_____

_____

_____

G. What historical events came after the time of this story?

_____

_____

_____

H. Look on a map. Find Israel, then Judah, then Bethlehem. Then find Moab, Ruth's homeland.

I. What is Moab's historical relationship to Israel?

_____

_____

_____

Day 4 - Summarize

A. Read the entire book, assigning a title to each chapter.

Chapter 1 _____

Chapter 2 _____

Chapter 3 _____

Chapter 4 _____

B. Write a short summary of the entire book of Ruth.

_____

_____

_____

_____

_____

_____

_____

_____

Finding Bible maps online:

- At www.biblemap.org, you can enter the book and chapter of the Bible that you are reading, and it will pinpoint any locations on the map for you.

- Go to http://www.biblestudy.org/maps/main.html. Scroll down and look for maps that are relevant to the story or passage you are studying.

- At www.bible.ca/maps/, scroll down the page and you will find a map covering the time of "Othniel, Ehud, and Ruth."

Day 5 - Themes and repeated words

Several words are repeated throughout the book of Ruth.

A. Read the entire book again, marking every appearance of the following words with a slanted red cross:

- Redeem

- Redeemer

- Kinsman

B. Read the explanation of a kinsman-redeemer from *The Nelson Study Bible* in the sidebar.

C. Review your markings and observations about the kinsman and redeemer in the book of Ruth.

Explain how Boaz fulfilled the role of kinsman-redeemer.

_____

_____

_____

_____

What was the result in the lives of Naomi and her daughter-in-law Ruth?

_____

_____

_____

_____

_____

Explain how Boaz's relationship to Naomi and Ruth is a picture of Christ's relationship to us.

_____

_____

_____

_____

_____

_____

Kinsman-Redeemer:

"The kinsman-redeemer was 'the defender of family rights.' This individual was a close relative who had the financial resources to rescue a poverty-stricken family member, stepping in to save that relative from slavery or from having to sell the family's ancestral land. In the story of Ruth, Boaz redeemed the land that Naomi was about to sell. He also took on another of the kinsman-redeemer responsibilities – the obligation of providing an heir for Ruth's deceased husband, Mahlon. Dying without an heir was considered a tragedy in the ancient Middle East. To rectify this situation, the brother of a deceased man was expected to marry the widow in order to produce a child, who would be considered the heir of the deceased. This was called a levirate marriage. Boaz willingly took on this duty, even though he was not the nearest relative (Ruth 3:12,13) He bought the land from Naomi, married Ruth, and carried on the family name through the birth of their son. Through all these actions Boaz exemplified the compassion and love of a redeemer. His life is an illustration for us of the compassion of Jesus, who is our Redeemer (Gal. 3:13)."

– From *The Nelson Study Bible*, NKJV

Day 6 - People in the story

Read the entire book one more time, this time **marking every mention of each of the following people**. Doing this will help you slow down and really pay attention to what each person is saying and doing.

Use the assigned color for each person, and mark the names and the pronouns (he, she, him, her, his, hers, etc.) that refer to each person. (You can do this in your Bible, or you may want to print out the text of Ruth from a computer.)

- Naomi (blue)
- Ruth (green)
- Boaz (purple)

Day 7 - Ruth's actions and words

A. When you have finished marking their names, go back and list Ruth's actions and words (in summary form). (For this study, we will be focusing on Ruth. At the end of this study, you'll find assignments related to Naomi and Boaz.)

_____

_____

_____

_____

_____

_____

_____

_____

_____

_____

_____

_____

B. Read Ruth 1:16. Remember Ruth was a Moabite woman. She lived in a land of idol worshippers. She tells Naomi, *"Your people shall be my people, and your God, my God."*

What is she declaring when she says this?

_____

_____

_____

C. Compare Ruth 2:12 with Ruth 3:9. What do these two verses share in common? What do you think this means?

_____

_____

_____

D. According to Boaz in Ruth 2:11, what did the people of Bethlehem know about Ruth?

_____

_____

E. Read Ruth 4:13-17. How is Ruth related to King David?

_____

Day 8 - Review

A. Use *Strong's Exhaustive Concordance* to find the meaning of Ruth's name:

_____

How does this meaning relate to the story of Ruth, Naomi, and Boaz?

_____

_____

_____

_____

B. Use *Strong's* to find the meaning of Boaz's name:

_____

How does this meaning relate to the story?

_____

_____

_____

C. Review what you learned in Day 5 about redeemers and Boaz. How does Ruth's response and relationship to Boaz as redeemer relate to our response and relationship to our redeemer, Jesus?

_____

_____

_____

_____

D. Using your notes from Day 7 and reviewing what you learned in Study 2, how does Ruth's life relate to what you learned from 1 Peter 3:3-4?

_____

_____

_____

_____

E. How does Ruth's life relate to what you learned from 1 Timothy 2:9-10 in Study 5?

_____

_____

_____

_____

F. Describe any similarities you see in how Ruth responded to Naomi's instructions and how Esther responded to instructions given to her by Mordecai, Hegai, and Ahasuerus. (See Study 4.)

_____

_____

_____

G. Describe any similarities you see in how Ruth spoke to Boaz and how Esther spoke to Ahasuerus in chapter 5, 7, and 8 of Esther. (See Study 4.)

_____

_____

_____

_____

H. Describe any similarities you see between Ruth's life and Sarah's life. (See Study 3.)

_____

_____

_____

_____

_____

_____

I. How did Ruth adorn herself? What good works did she perform? (See Study 6.)

_____

_____

_____

_____

J. Describe any similarities you see in how Ruth spoke to Boaz and how Abigail spoke to David in 1 Samuel 25. (See Study 8.)

_____

_____

_____

_____

K. How would you describe Ruth's character, based on her words and actions?

_____

_____

_____

_____

Day 9 - Comparing with Proverbs 31

Read Proverbs 31:10-31. This well-known passage closes with *"let her own works praise her in the gates"*. Ruth's works praised her *"in the gates"*. People knew and spoke about her works. They knew she had left her home to come to Bethlehem with her mother-in-law. They knew she had left behind the false gods of the Moabites to worship the true God. They knew how hard she was working to provide for Naomi and herself.

Review the list of actions that you recorded while reading the story of Ruth. These actions and words were the visible evidence of Ruth's virtuous character. As you read the Proverbs passage, **write down Ruth's actions and words next to the verses that describe similar actions and attitudes in the virtuous woman**. Record the reference of the verse in Ruth that mentions each action and attitude. (Not every verse will have a matching action from the story of Ruth. Some spaces on the chart will be left blank.)

Verse	Proverbs 31 (ESV)	Verse	Ruth
10	An excellent wife who can find? She is far more precious than jewels.		
11	The heart of her husband safely trusts in her and he will have no lack of gain.		
12	She does him good, and not harm, all the days of her life.		
13	She seeks wool and flax, and works with willing hands.		
14	She is like the ships of the merchant; she brings her food from afar.		
15	She rises while it is yet night and provides food for her household and portions for her maidens.		
16	She considers a field and buys it; with the fruit of her hands she plants a vineyard.		
17	She dresses herself with strength and makes her arms strong.		
18	She perceives that her merhandise is profitable. Her lamp does not go out at night.		

Verse	Proverbs 31 (ESV)	Verse	Ruth
19	She puts her hands to the distaff, and her hands hold the spindle.		
20	She opens her hand to the poor and reaches out her hands to the needy.		
21	She is not afraid of snow for her household, for all her household are clothed in scarlet.		
22	She makes bed coverings for herself; her clothing is fine linen and purple		
23	Her husband is known in the gates when he sits among the elders of the land.		
24	She makes linen garments and sells them; she delivers sashes to the merchant.		
25	Strength and dignity are her clothing, and she laughs at the time to come.		
26	She opens her mouth with wisdom, and the teaching of kindness is on her tongue		
27	She looks well to the ways of her household and does not eat the bread of idleness.		
28	Her children rise up and called her blessed; her husband also, and he praises her.		
29	"Many women have done excellently, but you surpass them all."		
30	Charm is deceitful, and beauty is vain, but a woman who fears the Lord is to be praised.		
31	Give her of the fruit of her hands, and let her works praise her in the gates.		

Day 10 - Application

A. Reread Proverbs 31:30-31. How does the life of Ruth demonstrate the truths of these verses?

_____

_____

_____

B. What do these verses say about **favor** or the opinion of others?

_____

_____

C. What do they say about physical **beauty**?

_____

_____

D. What do they say about **fearing God**?

_____

_____

E. What is more important to you in your everyday life – people's opinion of you, your appearance, or a proper love and fear of God?

_____

_____

F. Are you known by your works? Can others tell by your actions that you fear God? _____

G. ✽ What traits in Ruth's character are ones that you want to emulate?

_____

_____

_____

_____

_____

_____

_____

For further study:

- Finish studying the book of Ruth. List all of the actions and words of both Boaz and Naomi. Summarize the character of both people. Study the role of redeemer more fully. Read commentaries to better understand the full meaning of the book.

- Use a concordance to help you study "the fear of the Lord". What promises are associated with fearing God? What actions demonstrate one's fear of the Lord? After you organize your findings, review Ruth's life again. How is her fear of God demonstrated in the book of Ruth? How is it demonstrated in your life?

- Study the lives of other men and women in the Bible who are described as fearing God. Use the character study method that is outlined in Study 3, "Beauty in Trusting God."

- Do a word study of **kinsman/redeemer** (Strong's number H1350). Read and study other verses that use this word. Read Bible dictionaries and commentaries. What does it mean? What was the redeemer's role? How is the term used in reference to God? How is the term **redeemer** applied to Jesus? How is Boaz's relationship to Naomi and Ruth a picture of God and His people? How is his relationship a picture of Jesus redeeming His people from sin and death?

H. List specific actions that you, with God's help, will take to build the same character traits in your own life.

_____

_____

_____

_____

_____

_____

_____

_____

Beauty in Review

"Favour is deceitful, and beauty is vain: but a woman that feareth the Lord, she shall be praised. Give her of the fruit of her hands; and let her own works praise her in the gates." (Proverbs 31:30-31)

God describes true beauty in His Word. We have studied the lives of beautiful women. We have studied what Scripture says about physical beauty and how it can be wasted or abused. While studying beauty, we have also learned how to study the Bible. In this brief lesson, we will review what we have learned.

Day 1 - What is biblical beauty?

In your own notebook or journal, write a brief essay that summarizes God's definition of beauty. Consider the following questions:

- What is discretion?

- How does one gain discretion?

- How can a girl or woman act like a pig?

- In what ways can a woman display a lack of discretion?

- What actions and attitudes make a woman truly beautiful in God's eyes?

- What is the beautiful woman's attitude toward others?

- How does a beautiful and discreet woman treat men?

- What is the beautiful woman's attitude toward authority?

- What women in Scripture can we study as examples of godly beauty? What can we learn from them?

Day 2 - A truly beautiful woman

Think of a truly beautiful Christian woman that you know. Observe her and record your observations.

How does she respond to God's Word?

_____

_____

How does she interact with other people?

_____

Three important final steps for personal Bible study:

1. Review - What have I found in my study?

Invest some time in reviewing and organizing your notes. Make tables and charts, if that helps you more clearly organize your thoughts and observations. Write additional notes in the margins of your Bible.

2. Interpretation - What is God saying in this passage?

After you have done all your reading, studying, note-taking, and organizing, take time to look back over what you have found. What does it all mean? To ensure that you are on the right path in your interpretation of a passage, read one or two commentaries on it. Then write a summary of what the passage is saying.

3. Application - What am I going to do with what I have learned?

Pray for God's guidance How does He want you to change in your thinking and actions? What steps will you take to obey Him? Write down specific, measurable goals. Ask God for the grace to follow through. Review these goals on a regular basis. Ask someone else to hold you accountable.

Some books about godly beauty:

Beautiful Girlhood, revised by Karen Andreola

Becoming God's True Woman, by Nancy Leigh DeMoss and others

The Lost Art of True Beauty, by Leslie Ludy

Set Apart Femininity, by Leslie Ludy

Girl Talk, by Carolyn Mahaney and Nicole Whitacre

Raising Maidens of Virtue, by Stacy McDonald

The Beauty of Modesty, by David and Diane Vaughan

How does she serve others?

How does she treat her husband?

How does she treat her children?

How does she use her God-given talents?

How does she deal with disagreements?

How does she use her time?

How does she respond to trials and difficulties in her life?

How does she dress?

How does she look?

What can you do to get to know this woman better? How can you serve *her* and spend more time with her?

_____

_____

_____

Day 3 - Areas to grow in

✳ Is God calling you to become more beautiful in heart and soul? Are there specific areas in your life that you know, with the Holy Spirit's help, need to change? After seeking the guidance of God and your parents, outline a specific plan to help you grow in godly beauty. Then follow your plan!

_____

_____

_____

_____

_____

_____

_____

_____

Day 4 - Types of Bible study

What is the easiest study tool to use when doing a topical study? (See Study 6)

_____

_____

Explain how to study a Bible character. How can you find all the passages that tell about a specific person in the Bible? What kind of details should you look for as you read about the person? (See Study 3)

_____

_____

_____

_____

Listen to sermon audio from the web

Some pastors, like John Piper, have been making their sermons available online for decades, and many churches now offer downloadable recordings of their sermons. You can listen online from your computer, or save the audio recording to an MP3 player and listen to it in the car, while you work, or when you exercise.

Visit one of the following sites and listen to a sermon on beauty, or on any passage we have studied in this book:

- www.sermonaudio.com

- www.desiringGod.org

- www.wordMP3.com (some free, some paid)

- Your church's website

- Websites by other pastors or Bible teachers you respect

Explain how to study a book of the Bible. What different steps will help you better understand the book? How can you find background information on a book of the Bible? (See Studies 4 and 9)

_____

_____

_____

What six questions will help you meditate on a verse or passage of Scripture? (See Study 1)

_____

_____

What study tool can help you find the original Hebrew or Greek words used in a passage? How do you find the definition of those words? How do you find other verses that use the same word? (See Studies 5 and 6)

_____

_____

_____

_____

What helpful information is provided in a Bible's marginal notes? (see Study 7)

_____

_____

_____

Future study topics. At this point, and over time, you may think of other words, topics, passages, and people that you would like to study more. Use this area to record other studies you would like to pursue in the future. After you finish a study, you can refer to this list to find ideas for your next study.

_____

_____

_____

_____

_____

For additional study:

- Look up the following Strong's numbers in Strong's Exhaustive Concordance and study each of these Hebrew words that relate to beauty:

  • H2896

  • H3303

  • H3308

- Use the different methods you have learned in this book to study Proverbs 31:10-31 in detail.

- Study other women in the Bible, using the character study method outlined in Study 3. In what ways were they beautiful? In what ways did some abuse their God-given physical beauty?

Appendix

Alternate Questions for Young Men

Young men also need to learn about godly beauty from the Bible. Most of the questions in this book apply to both young ladies and young men. However, some are aimed directly to young ladies. These questions are marked with a star (✻). Young men completing these studies should refer to the alternate questions found in this section.

✻ What instructions are given to husbands? Are there any ways you can apply these instructions in relationships you have right now? (Think of your relationship with your mother, sisters, and other young ladies.)

Study 1, Day 5 G

✻ (skip this question)

Study 1, Day 6 B

✻ What is the Holy Spirit saying to you through your study of 1 Peter 2:13-3:9? Does your life reflect the kind of strong, quiet submission that Jesus demonstrated in His life? Are you compassionate and courteous? Are you willing to bless rather than returning evil for evil? Think about your relationship to the authorities in your life. Think about your attitudes and words toward your siblings and friends. In what areas do you need to change? Be specific.

Study 1, Day 7 B

_____

_____

_____

_____

_____

_____

✻ What sorts of things do women do to adorn themselves outwardly?

Study 2, Day 4 B

_____

_____

_____

_____

_____

What can women do to adorn themselves inwardly?

_____

_____

_____

_____

_____

Study 2, Day 6 A   ✽ Rewrite the quote from Matthew Henry, but skip the question.

Study 2, Day 6 B   ✽ Both people that Scripture specifically calls "meek" are men. Based on what you learned about "meekness" in this study, how can you put on godly meekness? In what ways do you need to grow? What will you do differently?

_____

_____

_____

_____

_____

_____

Study 3   ✽ (Optional) Instead of studying the life of Sarah, study Abraham's life. Answer questions throughout this study as they relate to Abraham.

Study 4, Day 14   ✽ In Esther's life, we can see the beauty of obedience, trusting the authorities over us, discretion, respectful appeal, patience, courage, understanding of the character of others, and the wise use of the opportunities, position, and talents that God grants us. We also see the examples of Ahasuerus, Mordecai, and Haman. What can you learn from the lives of each of these men? What qualities can you emulate? What qualities will you avoid, with the Holy Spirit's help?

_____

_____

_____

_____

_____

_____

_____

✻ The root word for sobriety is also used when the qualifications for elders are given in 1 Timothy 3:2 and Titus 1:8. What should sobriety look like when displayed by godly men in the church? How would this man handle responsibility? In what ways does he excercise self-control?

Study 5, Day 10 C

_____

_____

_____

_____

_____

_____

✻ Think of at least one godly man you know who exhibits this quality of sobriety.

Study 5, Day 10 D

Describe him.

_____

_____

_____

_____

_____

What can you do to get to know him better? Can you serve alongside him? Can you volunteer to help? Can you ask him to mentor you? Pray about this and then take action.

_____

_____

_____

_____

_____

_____

Study 5, Day 10 E

✱ Do you think you fit this description of a godly man and the ways he shows self-control? In what areas do you need to submit to God's changing work in your life?

_____

_____

_____

_____

Study 6, Day 6 C

✱ Do you invest more time and energy each day in serving others than you do in pursuing your own pleasure?

_____

_____

Study 7, Day 9 B, C

✱ Examine your own life:

Do you have associations with young ladies who behave like pigs? In what ways do they demonstrate their lack of discretion?

_____

_____

_____

_____

Read Proverbs 2:10-18 and Proverbs 5:1-5. What role does discretion play in your godly response to these young ladies?

_____

_____

_____

_____

_____

Read Genesis 39:7-12. How did Joseph respond to a woman who had no discretion?

_____

_____

_____

✱ Pray about what you have learned. In what ways is God calling you to think and behave differently?

Study 7, Day 9 D

_____

_____

_____

_____

✱ In this study, we saw how Abigail and David both showed discretion. In what similar ways can you show discretion in your own life? What can you learn from David's example of discretion? Think about relationships with siblings, parents, friends, and neighbors. List specific actions you will take.

Study 8, Day 12 C

_____

_____

_____

_____

_____

_____

✱ Review the attitudes and actions of both Nabal and David. What weaknesses do you see? What strengths? What similar weaknesses do you see in your own life? Apply what you have learned from this study to your own life. In what areas do you need to change? What specific actions, with God's help, can you take in obedience to His Holy Spirit's leading?

_____

_____

_____

_____

_____

_____

Study 9, Day 10 G

✳ Reread the entire book of Ruth, noting Boaz's words and actions. What can you learn from his example? How was he a godly man? What traits in Boaz's character do you want to emulate?

_____

_____

_____

_____

_____

_____

_____

_____

_____

Study 10, Day 3

✳ Is God calling you to change in your attitudes and actions toward young women? After seeking the guidance of God and your parents, outline a specific plan to help you become more mature and obedient in your relationships with young women.

_____

_____

_____

_____

_____

_____

_____